Institute of Biology:

The First
Fifty Years

Edited by Brian J Ford

Published to mark the Golden Jubilee
of the Institute of Biology,
20-22 Queensberry Place,
London SW7 2DZ

Institute of Biology: The First Fifty Years.

First published London, 2000.

© 2000 Institute of Biology
    Copyright reverts to contributors on publication

British Library Cataloguing in Publication Data
A Catalogue record of this book is available from the British Library.

ISBN 0 900490 37 3 (hardback)
ISBN 0 900490 38 1 (paperback)

Cover illustration: Darren Rackham

Typeset, printed and bound in Great Britain by
BJ's Print & Graphic Services Ltd.

Institute of Biology, 20-22 Queensberry Place, London SW7 2DZ

Contents

1. Introduction   1

i. Recollecting the Earliest Days   3
John Cloudsley-Thompson

2. Institute of Biology — Prior to Formation   7
Brian J Ford

ii. Memories of a President   15
John R Norris

3. The First Decade   19
Mike Buttolph

iii. A Committee Chairman Reflects   37
David R Morgan

4. Examining the Sixties   39
Bernard Thomason

iv. The Work of a Vice-President   53
Diana Anderson

5. Some Biology in the 1970s   55
Harry Grenville

v. At the Grass Roots   75
Marianne Overton

6. Into the Eighties 77
C U M Smith

vi. A Royal Society of Biology? 97
Sam Berry

7. A Millennium Ends 99
Wilson Wall

vii. Afterword 119
Sir Ghillean Prance

8. Appendices 121

INTRODUCTION

For 50 years the Institute of Biology has been the voice of British biology. In this specially commissioned book, the story of its birth in post-war Britain is told for the first time. Prime movers were Edward Hindle and Jim Danielli, who called the first general meeting in 1950. Over 150 people attended the Great Hall of King's College, London, to witness the birth of the Institute. We recall the Institute's 21st anniversary in 1971, when 1000 people attended a celebration meeting at Imperial College, and the 30th anniversary in January 1980 with a glittering occasion at the Natural History Museum.

The Institute's history is told decade by decade, with each chapter written by a member of the History of Biology Network. Our Editor is Brian J Ford, the Network Chairman at the Institute. A member of the Institute's public relations board and a member of Council for many years, he is a Fellow of Cardiff University and is the Royal Literary Fellow at the Open University. The 1950s are surveyed by Mike Buttolph, who studied microbial biochemistry and has held posts with the medical division of the Department of Health and Social Security, the University of London, the BBC, and Cranfield University. Bernard Thomason has compiled the chapter on the 1960s. He lectures on biology for Manchester Metropolitan University and is the recently appointed Honorary Archivist to the Institute of Biology. The 1970s have been covered by Harry Grenville, former Head of Biology at Repton School, previously a member of Council and one of our former Vice-Presidents, and the 1980s by Chris Smith of Aston University. He is better known as C U M Smith for a host of publications on brain science, its history, and philosophy. Finally, the last decade of the century is examined by Wilson Wall, an international consultant in genetics and the author of several popular science books.

The individual contributions that alternate with each chapter provide personal insights and reminiscences from different areas of Institute life. First is a section by John Cloudsley-Thompson, who worked under one of our Institute's founders, Jim Danielli, in the early 1950s, and reminds us of the era of our first General Secretary. The theme is continued in the section written by our outgoing President John Norris, who looks back on how he became a member and reflects on changing attitudes to biology.

A flavour of Council meetings is given in David Morgan's contribution, who reminds us all of the important role of the conferences organised by the Institute's committees. The Vice-President's view is contributed by Diana Anderson, who discusses the International Diploma in Toxicology of the Institute as an example of how we can offer accreditation in biology.

It is to our Branches that the Institute owes a particular debt of gratitude.

Marianne Overton contributes the view from the grass roots, with a word of encouragement for all members to contribute their energies and enthusiasms. Meanwhile, how can we bring the disciplines of biology together? Sam Berry looks back almost two decades, when the idea began to arise for a Royal Society of Biology. Federation of the many biological societies is a continuing preoccupation. It is one that will occupy our new President Sir Ghillean Prance, who offers the final word.

The Appendix section has been edited by Eric Carter, a former member of Council who has recently completed his term of office as the Institute's National Coordinator of Branches, with valued contributions from our Honorary Archivist, Bernard Thomason. Finally, the photographs have been collated by Nigel Cooper, Rector of Rivenhall and Silver End and a visiting fellow at the Centre for Theology and Society at Essex University.

This volume does not merely recount the internal working of the Institute of Biology, but sets it into its context. Developments in the biosciences, within the scientific community itself and the public at large, combine to tell a timely lesson on where biology stands. As this book reminds us, biology was the last of the sciences to be named, and the last to gain its own professional institute. Reading these chapters we can observe as the 'newcomer' emerges to dominate the realm of science in the 21st century. We are entering the era of biological revolution, and this book shows how biologists have coped with a changing world.

RECOLLECTING THE EARLIEST DAYS

John Cloudsley-Thompson CBiol FIBiol
Formerly Honorary Secretary, Biological Council, and
Emeritus Professor of Zoology, University of London

❝ Had it not been for the war I would have gained my PhD in 1945, but because of military service it was not until 20 June 1950 that I was awarded a PhD from Cambridge under the supervision of V B Wigglesworth FRS. On 1 July 1950, I was appointed to an assistant lectureship in zoology at King's College, University of London, at the top grade of £600 pa + £50 per child. We had two sons then, and a third was born in 1952. My pay rose to £650 (equivalent to about £14 000 in 2000) when I became a lecturer at the age of 30 the following year.

My professor was Jim Danielli, who later became a very good friend. Jim was a founding member of the Institute of Biology. He urged me to join, but I could not afford to then — we let rooms to students to earn extra money and my wife, Anne, a physiotherapist, stood in three evenings a week for the superintendent of the clinic of the Royal National Institute for the Blind. We were at the beginning of what my bank manager afterwards described as 10 years of a gradually increasing overdraft.

I still remember the first General Secretary of the Institute of Biology, Fielding Clarke, and his office in the basement of Tavistock House South. He was not seen as being very efficient and Jim Danielli told me that he had been appointed largely because Jim had been told that he was not very good at interviews. In fact, Jim felt this was the only thing he *was* good at! Danielli had quite a sharp tongue at times. He had joined the Communist Party during his undergraduate days, but afterwards changed his mind. Even so, he could not get a visa to visit the USA for many years afterwards, which he found most trying.

Jim Danielli knew that I had become interested in deserts since serving with the Seventh Armoured Division, (the 'Desert Rats') in 1941–42, so he invited me to be the convenor of an Institute of Biology symposium on *The biology and productivity of hot and cold deserts,* held at the Royal Institution, Albemarle Street, on 25–27 September 1952. The symposium was opened by the President of the Institute, Edward Hindle, who was always most kind and helpful to me. Danielli liked him too, I think, and clearly disapproved when I remarked that I thought the bust of Hindle, made for the Institute, made him look rather like a gorilla (see page 60).

The costs of the symposium, the fares of overseas invited speakers and the subsequent publication of the proceedings were financially supported by UNESCO, of which the formidable Julian Huxley was Director-General. In the event, the book *Biology of Deserts: The Proceedings of a Symposium on the Biology of Hot and Cold Deserts Organised by the Institute of Biology* was not published until 1954. I was the editor, and it seemed to take an eternity to appear. The volume was experimental in that it was not typeset in the normal way of those days, but was typed by a secretary of the Royal Society named Tessa Tippett. I do not think that much cost was incurred by the Institute. The price was set at 10 shillings (five shillings to members) plus sixpence postage. The book was well reviewed by *Nature* and the discussions were described as 'little gems', or something like that. I often went from King's College to Burlington House to meet Dax Copp and see how much progress was being made. I got to know Dax very well in those days. He was the ideal person for General Secretary and a really good friend.

Early in the 1950s I succeeded J Z Young as Honorary Secretary of the Biological Council and wrote up the minutes, which are still in the possession of the Institute of Biology. W P K Findlay was the chairman, a position I was to hold in 1977–82. On behalf of the Council I wrote a letter entitled 'The learned societies', which was published in *The Times* (21 March 1953). As I indicated in an article for our journal (Cloudsley-Thompson, 1995), academic biologists were rather few in number in those days and even junior lecturers such as myself had the opportunity to meet most of the eminent members of our profession in a way that would not be possible now that we are so numerous. People like J B S Haldane and P A Buxton, who were such formidable opponents of other eminent biologists, with whom they clashed at scientific meetings, could not have been kinder and more generous with their ideas to people like me.

Others whom I met through the various symposia of the Institute, beginning with *The numbers of man and animals* (held on 24 – 25 September 1954 and published in 1955), were J B Cragg, a most vivacious and amusing personality. I thoroughly enjoyed taking part in the lively discussions which invariably followed the lectures. Other friends of the time were Kenneth Mellanby, Maurice Solomon, Donald Gunn, Howard Hinton, John Ebling, Gyp Wells, and many others. Both Carl Pantin and Eric Smith had taught me at Cambridge, but I really got to know them when they came to Khartoum as external examiners during the period I was professor there. The same applies to Ernest Barrington and Jakes Ewer. No matter how eminent these people

The Institute's London conversazione, 1958. H D G Roper and M Spenser, students from the National College of Food Technology, with John Cloudsley-Thompson (centre) are shown new dehydrated food samples by J F Hearne of the Ministry of Agriculture, Fisheries and Food.

were, and how great the controversies between them, they were always most helpful and supportive to the young biologists on the way up.

The Institute played a role by organising meetings at which people could get to know one another, which helped increase the networks of friends. One of the local Institute events which was always incredibly well attended was the annual London Branch conversazione. I was convenor of one or two of these, and was asked by the editors of *Nature* to write an account of the Institute of Biology conversazione of 1957 (Cloudsley-Thompson, 1957). I feel sure that one of the reasons why such events as congresses and conversaziones were so popular in those days was that people did not travel so much and consequently were more inclined to regard such events as enjoyable excursions, particularly because the war was still fresh in everyone's minds. **99**

References

Cloudsley-Thompson (1957) Institute of Biology Conversazione. *Nature*, **180,** 319 – 320.

Cloudsley-Thompson J (1995) The book that most … . *Biologist,* **42,** 80.

INSTITUTE OF BIOLOGY— PRIOR TO FORMATION

Brian J Ford FLS CBiol FIBiol
Chairman, History of Biology Network, and
Royal Literary Fellow at the Open University Business School

Half a century ago few people took biology seriously. Bacteriology was winding down, confident that all the major infections were on the point of defeat. Teaching was regarded as the major sector of employment for graduate biologists. Medical schools began to state a preference for students with A-level passes in chemistry, physics, and mathematics to those with biology in the list. Official bodies did not rate biology as a 'real' science.

During Brian Heap's presidency, one of the tasks I was asked to undertake was presenting the case for the retention of our name when there were pressures to add 'biosciences', or something similar, to our title. It drew my attention to the fact that biology is itself a relatively recent arrival on the academic scene. Our subject was indeed the last major discipline to be recognised. The others were part of the language many centuries ago. 'astronomy' (1205) and 'medicine' (1225) being the first. 'Physics', at the time encompassing a far broader catchment, was coined in 1598 and 'chemistry' followed in 1605. 'Biology' was mooted by the German philosopher Treveranus in 1802, and did not emerge in its modern English form until 1810. The fact that today's membership (and our affiliated societies) overwhelmingly prefer to retain the term 'biology' demonstrates fittingly that the science has truly come of age.

The changing role of biology

In its earlier years, biology was centred on the identification of the living world and the study of natural history. The result was a reductionist imperative encouraging biologists to search for increasingly smaller categorisations in our attempt to unravel reality. This may explain the abundance of biological societies, which proliferated like subgroups in a taxonomic key. The other sciences — physics, chemistry, astronomy — soon centred on a single learned body, while biology spawned hundreds of specialised societies.

How could they be drawn together? Discussions on the unifying of British biology began during the Second World War. At the Biochemical Society in 1944 the discussion centred on the possibility of bringing the major biological societies together, and on 22 September 1944 a meeting was held at the Royal Society to find a way forward. The result was the formation of the Biological Council, and one of the topics under discussion was the idea of an Institute of Biology. It was a curious time. University degrees were condensed into a scant two years in order to rush through a new generation of graduates after the depletion inflicted by war. Scientists were greatly in demand. Sir David Attenborough now recalls that, when he joined the Navy to do his national service, he stated that he had studied trilobites for his degree. His chief petty officer told him that this was the ideal qualification — and promptly appointed him to instruct new entrants on astronomical navigation.

An Institute is proposed

On 15 April 1946, at a meeting of the Association of British Zoologists (now the Zoological Society), discussion turned to the possible formation of a professional institute for all biologists. At their next meeting, on 17 May, the following resolutions were carried:
- That this meeting considers that a professional Institute of Biology (Biologists) is desirable.
- That an account of the proceedings be submitted to the Biological Council with a request that the Council should explore the matter and formulate proposals.

Chairing this meeting was Edward Hindle FRS, who was to become our first President. Discussions continued throughout the summer and on 18 October 1946 the Biological Council agreed the following resolution:

'After some discussion the Council considered that the demand for an Institute of Biology, brought forward by the Association of British Zoologists and others, was not yet proven but the Council considered

that the matter should be examined in greater detail and asked Danielli to make a further report after he had consulted with Edward Hindle (President of the Association of British Zoologists) and C B Williams (Association of Applied Biologists)'.

Jim Danielli, who had qualified in chemistry at University College London and worked on cell membranes and cytochemistry, took the next crucial stages. He was

Professor J F Danielli, first Honorary Secretary 1949–53.

Jim Danielli's draft for the circular letter, corrected in his own hand, that was sent out to society secretaries to seek interest in a possible new Institute.

Letter for Secretaries

Dear

The Biological Council has undertaken to discover whether there is a demand for an Institute of Biology, and to do this must obviously circularise the members of its constituent Societies.

I shall be very much obliged if you could inform me whether there would be any objection to your Society enclosing with the next distribution of documents to its members the enclosed papers, which will be provided for you by the Council.

You will appreciate that The object is simply to discover whether the biologists wish for an Institute, and that there is no question of approval or disapproval by your Society is involved.

Since the documents must be printed I should be grateful if you could let me know before April 30th June 15th whether you can circulate them, and how many, when you would require, and to what address they should be sent.

Yours sincerely,

By agreeing corresponding distributing our circular your Society will not be committed in any way to itself supporting the self scheme.

based in Cambridge during the war, where one of his PhD students was Peter Mitchell (who won the Nobel Prize for Chemistry in 1978). In the post-war years, Danielli was at the Chester Beatty Research Institute and Professor of Zoology at University College London. He was to become the first Honorary Secretary of the Institute, a post he held until 1953. In the 1960s he moved to the USA, and he died in 1984. He was immortalised by a slip of the tongue by Jack de Manio on the BBC *Today* programme, who famously announced: 'Professor Danielli has created an entirely new form of orgasm. I'm sorry, that should have been organism…'

Danielli drafted a letter asking for comments and the typescript was corrected by hand. It survives in our archives, along with a circulation list to the Physiological Society, the Genetical Society, the Association of Applied Biologists, the Marine Biological Association, the Pathological Society, the Royal Entomological Society and the Biochemical Society. The Royal Horticultural Society (RHS) and the Eugenics Society were considered too, but it was felt that the Eugenics Society would represent too few biologists, while the 30 000 membership of the RHS was too large. In the event, 24 copies were sent for circulation to the RHS Council.

The resulting report was ready in April, and on 30 May 1947 the Biological Council was formally asked to send round a circular. They demurred, asking Danielli to set out further details of what the Institute was for and what exactly it could do. His handwritten notes, preserved in the Institute's archives, set out the first formal concept for the Institute:

'At present biologists have no effective professional organisation. This report will, we hope, reach practically all biologists in Britain. We ask that all biologists *will return this form* [altered to] should read this report with care, and return the form at the end of the report. When these returns are received it will be possible to see whether the time has arrived to form an Institute.

'There are two aspects of an Institute, which are of general interest: on the one hand there is the daily life of an Institute; and on the other hand there is the long-term influence of an Institute on policy. The setting up of an Institute would immediately give to biologists a central address and general office service, and should ultimately provide a club and meeting rooms. It would produce a bulletin to carry news and notes, maintain a watch on legislation and international matters of interest to biologists, maintain an employment bureau, and protect the standards of employment of its members, if need be by providing legal aid. A public relations service would be maintained, members would be advised on their dealings with the press and with publishing firms. Special income tax problems would be considered, and the establishment of special relationships with trading firms and with insurance offices would be sought. Such day-to-day activities constitute a group of sound reasons for forming an Institute…'

Controversy

By this time the idea of an Institute was fast gaining ground, and sometimes it seemed as if the rate of progress was giving the participants feelings of grandeur. Harold Kaplan wrote in glowing terms to Danielli from the Massachusetts State College on 28 January 1948. 'As editor of the *American Society of Professional Biologists News* … I would be very pleased if you would consent to contribute a brief paper to our next issue. We have read in *Nature* about a proposed British Institute of Biology,' he wrote. 'We would appreciate a statement from you concerning the British Institute of Biology for *ASPB News*. [The article] should be limited to about 500 words, although more is acceptable.'

Can you imagine how this news was received? Here was a chance to advance our cause to the audience of one of America's bright new societies. It was a most valuable opportunity for public relations in a highly reputable area of influence, but Danielli wrote back tersely: 'I should prefer to defer taking any action in this until things have proceeded a little further with the British Institute of Biology.' He added, with a hint almost of disdain: 'I shall be in touch with you again as soon as I feel the moment is opportune.'

There was controversy at home, too. On 26 February 1948 J Z Young wrote to

Teething troubles beset the nascent Institute. This original letter from J Z Young exemplifies the difficulties experienced in the early days.

UNIVERSITY COLLEGE LONDON
DEPARTMENT OF ANATOMY   GOWER STREET, W.C.1

EUSton 4400
Professor J. Z. Young,
M.A., F.R.S.

February 26th, 1948

Dear Jim,

I have been trying to get you all day. I gather you want to know whether I feel that the report on the Institute could go forward as a report from the Secretaries and the answer is that if I am responsible it cannot be so. However, I did not put it forward, if you wish, as from the members who agree with it? As I think my secretary told you on the 'phone I have serious objections and cannot imagine that I should be prepared to agree to putting forward a proposal in this form on behalf of the Council, and might in fact think it necessary to resign if the Council decide to sponsor this scheme as it stands at present.

Yours sincerely,

Dr.J.F.Danielli,
Chester Beatty Research Institute,
Royal Cancer Hospital,
Fulham Road, S.W.3.

Danielli: 'I have been trying to get you all day. I gather you want to know whether I feel that the report on the Institute could go forward as a report from the Secretaries and the answer is that if I am responsible it cannot be so. However, I did not know that I was on the committee. Why not put it forward, if you wish, as from the members who agree with it? As I think my secretary told you on the phone I have serious objections and cannot imagine that I would be prepared to agree to putting

Jim Danielli's draft for the letter that was to be circulated to canvass support.

Covering Letter

The enclosed memorandum, proposing the formation of an Institute of Biology, has been drawn up by the Biological Council. We are in general agreement with the proposal, and if an Institute is formed will give full support to its activities. But, as is pointed out in the memorandum, it will not be feasible unless at least six hundred biologists are prepared to join the Institute at its become foundation members of the Institute. We therefore appeal to all biologists to complete and return the form at the end of the memorandum. We particularly ask that no one should all when announce the an intention of supporting the Institute should agree to do so for a minimum period of seven years.

The first report setting out the Institute's aims and aspirations. Danielli corrected it, prior to its being printed by the Biological Council.

An Institute of Biology

At present biologists have no effective professional organisation. This report puts forward the reasons for establishing an Institute of Biology. This report will, we hope, reach practically all biologists in Britain. We ask that all biologists should read this report with care, and return the form at the end of the report. When these returns are received it will be possible to see whether the time has arrived to form an Institute.

There are two aspects of an Institute which are of general interest : on the one hand there is the daily life of an Institute ; and on the other hand there is the long-term influence of an Institute on policy. the setting up of an Institute would immediately give to biologists a central address and general office service, and should ultimately provide a club and meeting rooms.

forward a proposal in this form on behalf of the Council, and might in fact think it necessary to resign if the Council decide to sponsor this scheme as it stands at present.'

Canvassing support

The Biological Council approved the final document on 19 March 1948. Over 7000 copies were printed for circulation. A detachable form at the end, returnable to 'Dr J F Danielli at the Chester Beatty Research Institute', invited recipients to indicate whether they might join or not, and to add remarks or suggestions. Of the 7000 recipients, almost 10 per cent offered supportive responses. The figures were presented at a meeting of the Biological Council at the Royal Society's rooms on 10 November 1948. The meeting was told that about 650 replies had been received, of which over 500 were in support of the formation of an Institute. A subcommittee, including Hindle, Danielli, and Harris, would convene a meeting to establish the new body. On 4 December 1948 *Nature* published an article: 'A proposed Institute of Biology, by Dr J F Danielli'. The article makes stirring reading. 'No such foundation [as the Institutes serving physicists, chemists, etc] exists to serve the needs of biologists… If support is forthcoming, the Biological Council will call a central meeting of biologists, at which officers and a provisional council can be elected.'

Much of the article was a reprint of the document previously circulated, and its effect was immediate. Everyone interested in the idea was soon aware of the plans now afoot, and the future of the Institute seemed set.

A crucial meeting

On 1 February 1949 the Biological Council set up a Provisional Council for the new Institute, with Hindle as Chairman, Danielli as Honorary Secretary, and R J C Harris as Assistant Secretary. The Provisional Council met at the Institute of Physics on the afternoon of 28 October 1949 to make arrangements for this, the first general meeting. The minutes of that meeting, headed 'Institute of Biology', were the first such document to dignify our new name. Hindle opened the meeting at 2.30pm and welcomed a group of eminent biologists.

Hindle spelled out the background to the proposal, stressing the clear evidence of a need for the Institute and thanking those who had helped bring it so close to fruition. He referred to one or two biologists who had been invited to become members of the Provisional Council but who had declined (Julian Huxley and Sir Paul Fildes), before Danielli was confirmed as Honorary Secretary, at least until 1 October 1950. The meeting decided on the agenda for the inaugural general meeting, with items covering the aims, publications policy, the formation of Local Branches, and establishment of an Appointments Register. Donations had been received from the Society for Experimental Biology (who gave £10, worth about £240 as this book goes to press), the Biochemical Society (£5, now £125) and the Biological Council itself (£20, now £480). It was agreed that applications for membership would be accompanied by a fee of one guinea (£1.05, currently worth about £25).

On 12 November 1949 a subcommittee of the Provisional Council met to agree final details for the inaugural meeting and the form of application for admission to membership. There were even notes for the guidance of candidates. The meeting was originally set for Friday 6 January 1950, but was later brought forward by one day. Notice of the forthcoming meeting was published in *Nature*, and printed copies of the documents were circulated in December to everyone who had indicated support.

There was now no looking back. The people had been marshalled, and the growing desire for the formation of an Institute had been properly documented. On 5 January 1950 the inaugural general meeting was due, and the Institute of Biology was about to be born.

Acknowledgements

Our outgoing President, John Norris, initiated the writing of this book and he has assisted in editing and with invaluable advice. Among the Presidents from whose friendship I have benefited are the late Ronald Keay, Brian Heap, Peter Biggs, Sir Colin Spedding, Alan Hibbert, and Sir Ghillean Prance. At headquarters, I am particularly grateful to Alan Malcolm, Chief Executive; Chris Fox, Personal Assistant; Chandra Mohan, Head of Management Services; Sam Mardell, Editorial Co-ordinator; Alison Bailey, Head of Journals; and Helen Benson, Production Editor, for their practical assistance at every turn.

MEMORIES OF A PRESIDENT

John R Norris CBE CBiol FIBiol
Past-President, Institute of Biology

66 In 1950, the year the Institute was founded, I was a first-year student at the Bacteriology Department of the University of Leeds. My professor explained that I had made a poor choice of subject, since in his view microbiology was all but finished. His argument was simple and compelling: there were many bacteria about, but there were only a few that caused human disease. We had antibiotics to control most of these and given about five years we would be able to treat all of them — and then the subject would be finished. This was not, of course, a message I wished to hear on my first day as a student.

Dr John Norris, President 1998–2000.

I need not have worried; even as he spoke Crick, Watson, and their colleagues were deciphering the structure of DNA, and I experienced the excitement that ran through an audience packing the Great Hall and filling two overflow lecture theatres to hear Francis Crick. Far from being dead, biology and particularly microbiology were poised on the threshold of their most exciting and productive phase.

Those days were heady, stimulating times for biologists for the whole subject was opening up in new directions. It is difficult to convey the sense of excitement experienced by research workers studying under what would now be regarded as primitive conditions, when preparing a meat extract agar plate meant exactly that — starting with the meat. Thin layer chromatography was a messy business resembling pasting and hanging wallpaper, while starch gel electrophoresis, an equally messy and indeed dangerous process, represented the cutting edge of analytical technology. But exciting and stimulating it certainly was, and it was against the background of that excitement that the Institute of Biology was born.

I joined the Institute in 1969 looking for a way to broaden my knowledge of the natural world so that I could see my research in better perspective. I learned a great deal through participation in Institute events, both at the Local Branch level and centrally. A residential course at Pitlochry on the agricultural economy of the Highlands and a two-day Mason conference in 1986, sponsored by the Institute, on *Biology and Industry* were just two of the events I attended that demonstrated the unique ability of the Institute to network across the different disciplines of biology.

As I read this story of the Institute's first 50 years two things strike me: the way the Institute has responded to change and the way themes have recurred during the half-century. From the very beginning critics of the Institute maintained that it was largely composed of old-fashioned naturalists with little interest in 'real science'. This was never true, as an examination of the programmes of the Branches and of the Institute itself will readily demonstrate. The Institute has always built bridges between members working at the forefront of laboratory-based research and those whose interests are in more applied aspects of the subject: ecology, teaching, agriculture, the environment, and medicine, for example. This networking continues. The Institute, in co-operation with some of its affiliated societies, has, for instance, recently held a successful symposium on *The biology of air pollution,* bringing together leading experts from the medical, biochemical, environmental, and agricultural fields, which was followed by a Parliamentary reception at which the main themes emerging from the conference were put to interested politicians.

Chartered status served to emphasise the important responsibility of the Institute to care for the welfare of its members. Fifty years ago there were many who considered that biology was not a 'proper' science like chemistry or physics, but as the 20th century drew to its close, the central role of biology as a determinant of the future of society has become increasingly evident. With this awareness has come concern on the part of the public and increased legislation and control by Government. It is impossible today for schoolchildren and students to carry out many of the experimental procedures that formed a central part of my education in biology.

The Institute has accepted its responsibility for defending the integrity of its members and works closely with the regulatory agencies to try to ensure that legitimate safety concerns and requirements for quality assurance in higher education do not lead to unreasonably restrictive legislation.

The Institute has put increasing effort into the public understanding of biology. This has been particularly effective at Branch level where open meetings often attract sizeable audiences. The last few years have seen a large number of consultative documents submitted to the Institute by Government and its agencies, and the effectiveness of the Institute in consolidating views of its affiliated societies in responding to these initiatives has often been acknowledged by Government both in Britain and Europe.

Also, we have increased the level of our contact with the media. The closing year of the 20th century saw more than 150 media contacts and our Chief Executive has frequently been interviewed, particularly on controversial food issues.

The importance of taking a holistic approach to biology has long been recognised in our centres of higher education, where the traditional discipline-based departments — such as botany, zoology, genetics, microbiology and biochemistry — have largely been subsumed into wide-ranging bio-sciences departments. This recognition of change in the shape of biology has not yet been reflected in the organisation of the professional bodies and learned societies. This tradition of fragmentation makes it difficult for biology to contribute a single, clear voice to the public and regulatory debates that are becoming such an important part of our lives.

As the Institute enters its second half-century it is actively taking the lead in attempting to draw together the various bodies involved in the biosciences. As the 20th century ended, an Institute paper entitled *The Institute of Biology — into the new millennium* stimulated discussion of these issues across the bioscience community and generated considerable support for further integration, so continuing the processes of change and development that have been a hallmark of the Institute during its first 50 years.

Mankind, having learned largely to control — and possibly to destroy — its external environment, is now embarked on an even greater adventure: the modification of its own internal environment. The tools to enable us to do this have been provided by developments in genetics and cell biology that have taken place during the Institute's first half-century. The results of applying these tools during its second half-century will be profound both for science and for society. As we try to look ahead we have to recognise that our view of the future is probably no clearer than was that of our founding fathers 50 years ago.

Only two things are certain: the tensions between biology and society will increase, at least in the short term, and the Institute will continue to occupy a pivotal position at the interface between the two. The young scientist entering our profession at the start of the 21st century can look forward with confidence to a half-century that will be at least as stimulating as the one described in this book. **99**

THE FIRST DECADE

Mike Buttolph PhD CBiol MIBiol
Consultant and Visiting Lecturer in the Division of Life Sciences
at King's College, London

The birth of the Institute of Biology at the start of 1950 took place when the national situation was a strange mixture of bleakness and hope. The war was won, but the national economy was in a parlous state and the international situation was threatening. The Labour Government had just devalued the pound, from $4.03 to $2.80. Milk, eggs, and meat were rationed — the meat ration had been halved in 1949 — and there were fuel crises and widespread shortages. It was calculated that, on average, every woman in the country was spending an hour a day in a queue. There was little unemployment, but there was a wage-freeze in force, entered into by the Government and the Trades Union Congress (TUC) in 1948.

The world was in a state of cold war. In Churchill's phrase, an iron curtain had descended across Europe. Germany and Austria were each divided into zones occupied by the Russians and Western powers. The North Atlantic Treaty Organisation had been created in 1949, and in the same year Russia started a series of tests of atomic weapons. Albert Einstein caught the mood of the times with his prediction that 'general annihilation beckons'. On the other hand, things could only get better, and indeed they had started to do so in some ways. In 1950 the Labour Government was in power with a large majority, and they had already done much to implement the promised programme of widespread nationalisation and social reform, including the creation of the National Health Service.

The inaugural meeting

This was the background to the principal milestone in the creation of the new Institute, the first general meeting on 5 January 1950. It was held in the Great Hall of King's College, London, in the Strand. Over 150 people attended, and the chair was taken by Edward Hindle. Hindle was an

Dr Edward Hindle, first President of the Institute 1950–52.

The first decade

The founder-President responds to the draft of the minutes of the first general meeting. Note the call for genetics to be represented on Council – a prescient suggestion in the light of present-day developments.

entomologist specialising in tropical diseases. He had served in the Army in the First World War and carried out research at several centres in the UK and overseas. During 1944–51 he was Scientific Director of the Zoological Society of London, during which time he co-ordinated the arrangements for the founding of the Institute of Biology. Hindle was involved in the running of many scientific bodies, for example as General Secretary of the British Association for the Advancement of Science (1946–51) and President of the Universities Federation for Animal Welfare (from 1944 until his death in 1973).

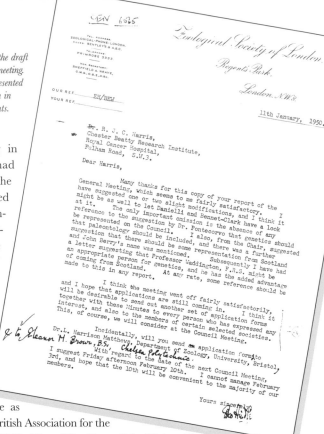

In his opening statement to this historic gathering, Hindle began by reminding the meeting of the proposal first made in 1946 by the Association of British Zoologists that there should be formed an 'Institute of Biology (Biologists)'. He reported that the Biological Council had set up a Provisional Council for the new Institute, with Hindle as Chairman, Jim Danielli as Honorary Secretary and R J C Harris as Assistant Secretary.

Most of the business of the meeting was straightforward. The proposed membership of Council was approved, with suggestions that representatives of various interests should be co-opted. Hindle was elected President, the draft aims and objects were approved, and it was agreed that there should be a 'salary census' and a register of consultants. Danielli said that the original proposal for two grades of membership had been much criticised. Council therefore proposed that there should be one category of membership, the essential qualification being an honours degree in a biological subject, or equivalent experience. This single grade for qualified members continued until Fellowship was introduced in 1963. The meeting also agreed that Council would elect the members, and should consider establishing student membership. The launch of the Institute attracted widespread interest, and there were reports of the first general meeting in *Nature* and the *Chemist and Druggist* in January 1950. One thousand reprints of the *Nature* report were ordered to be sent to members and prospective members. The Council meeting in February 1950 co-opted four people to represent the interests of some biological specialities, and Scotland, so that Council had 21 members, seven per cent of the total membership of the Institute.

In February 1950 there was a general election, which returned a Labour Government with a small majority. They nationalised the steel industry and the economic situation worsened. The meat ration was further reduced, to about 20 g per day. In May 1950 Council of the new Institute met for the second time. The meeting 'could not agree that membership of the Parliamentary and scientific committee would serve any useful purpose'. This seems curious for an organisation dedicated to elevating the profession of biologist and the advancement and diffusion of a knowledge of biology. Sure enough, by October 1950 Council decided that it would, after all, like to join the Parliamentary and scientific committee. By that time there was not enough money to pay the subscription, and it was not until 1953 that the cost of joining could actually be raised.

First conference

The Institute held its first conference in October 1950. It was a joint meeting with the Association of Atomic Scientists on *The biological hazards of atomic energy*. The timeliness of the topic brought the new Institute to the attention of a wider public. The subject for the conference was inspired, since it was of direct interest to scientists in several different fields, and it was also a matter of increasing concern to the general public. The world was still coming to terms with the idea of the atomic bomb. The Americans were developing and producing nuclear weapons, Britain had its own development programme and, as we have seen, a test detonation had been carried out in Russia during the previous year. At the same time, there were predictions that peaceful uses of atomic energy would bring massive benefits, particularly in power generation and medical diagnosis and treatment.

Furthermore, Britain was a world leader, not only in the application of the new nuclear technologies, but also in controlling the associated hazards. The first recommendations on risk control had been drawn up in Britain as long ago as 1921, and the first international meeting on the subject had been held in London in 1925. In 1950, the latest recommendations had been issued by the International Commission on Radiological Protection, again held in London. Many of the world's leading experts were to be found in British universities and research centres.

The conference was held on two days in October 1950 at the Royal Institution in London. It was arranged by Alexander (later Sir Alexander) Haddow, who had qualified in medicine in Edinburgh and carried out work on chemical carcinogenesis before moving to the Chester Beatty Research Institute in London in 1936. Here he had encountered Danielli. Ten years later Haddow was made Director of the Chester Beatty, a post he held until he retired in 1969. He was a member of Council 1950–52, was knighted in 1966, and died in 1976.

The four sessions of this pioneering conference were chaired by Sir Henry Dale, Sir John Cockroft, Sir Ernest Rock Carling, and Lord Boyd-Orr. The speakers included many of the world's leading authorities — L H Gray, E E Pochin, W V Mayneord, R M Sievert, J F Loutit, C D Darlington, Kenneth Mather, E B Ford, Guido Pontecorvo, Sir George Thomson and Kathleen Lonsdale. Although there were 500 places available, they were heavily oversubscribed. Several reports of the meeting appeared in the media, including an item in the BBC programme *Science Survey*, and the proceedings, edited by Haddow, were published in 1952 by Oxford University Press. The new Institute still had only 500 members, but this first conference brought it publicity out of all proportion to its size.

Balancing the books

Although the conference was considered a great success in so many respects, it had cost the Institute well over £100 (more than £2000 in present-day values). This was

reported to the meeting of Council in December 1950, and at the same meeting the Treasurer, R J C Harris, reported: 'An average monthly expenditure of not less than £100 must be expected, and it is urgently necessary to consider how to cover this.' Most of the ideas to ameliorate the financial situation centred around gaining more members. By this time there were 531 members, still paying one guinea (£1.05, currently over £20) for the year from October 1950, although some 200 subscriptions were still outstanding.

In fact, the financial situation was precarious throughout the first few years of the Institute's existence. In January 1951 there was £540 in the bank, and expenditure for the month was £220. The Treasurer noted: 'At the present rate of

Professor R C J Harris, first Treasurer of the Institute, and President 1978–79.

41 Queen's Gate, London SW7: the Institute's first home.

expenditure, the Institute could just carry on, but very substantial increases were necessary if increased services were to be given to members, and fresh activities developed.' The situation was much the same for the national economy: British people everywhere were having to pay more. In 1951 the Budget introduced charges for spectacles and false teeth. This drove a coach and horses through the principle that the new National Health Service would not levy charges on the public. As a protest, in April 1951 Aneurin Bevan and Harold Wilson resigned from the Government, which continued in power until October of that year.

Many of the Institute's continuing problems could be linked to its growing financial commitments, yet it continued to make steady progress. In June 1950 it was resolved to appoint a General Secretary at an annual salary of £550, and in November that year the Institute took up offices at Tavistock House, the British Medical Association's building in Bloomsbury, at an annual rent of £100. Council meetings, which had been held at the Institute of Physics in Belgrave Square, were transferred to the Institute's offices at Tavistock House from October 1951.

The Institute's accommodation had to be increased twice more during the 1950s,

Tavistock House, Tavistock Square, London WC1: initial temporary base of the Institute.

on each occasion with a corresponding strain on the budget. In 1955 the Institute took the lease of the fourth floor at 41 Queen's Gate in Kensington, the premises of the Royal Entomological Society. In 1958 more space was needed and the lease was extended to include the fifth floor of the building. The move to Queen's Gate in 1955 involved the Institute in paying an extra £150 annually in rent. It was calculated that in three years' time this extra cost would be covered by additional income from subscriptions, and for the time being, the gap was bridged by a fund-raising exercise in which industrial firms donated a total of £405 (over £8000 at the present time).

Administration

When the Institute started, R J C Harris had carried out the administrative work in his spare time. Harris had graduated in chemistry at Imperial College and by 1950 was working with Haddow at the Chester Beatty Research Institute in Chelsea, so Haddow arranged for the Institute to have the use of a small office close by, in premises in Onslow Gardens that were owned by the Chester Beatty. At this time Harris was working on chemical carcinogenesis, but later his main work was on the viruses associated with cancer, and he became Director of the Microbiological Research Establishment at Porton Down in 1971. He worked for the Institute in one capacity or another (and often in more than one capacity at the same time) from its inception until he became President in 1978–79. He died in 1980 at the age of 58.

The administrative work generated by the new Institute increased rapidly. Although it was difficult to cover the costs, it had been recognised that a full-time General Secretary was urgently required. The post was extensively advertised in *Nature*, the *Daily Telegraph*, and *The Times* in June 1950. In due course, after lengthy selection and interview procedures, A Fielding Clarke was appointed to the post on a salary of £550 pa with effect from 1 September 1950. It seemed a happy appointment but, as we shall see, controversy soon arose and he was to leave in less than a year.

Time of turbulence

Early in 1951 the Government published a report on the supply and demand for professional biologists. Briefly, this said that there would be about 2500 new jobs for biologists in the period 1950–54, when the universities would produce about 3400 biology graduates. In an editorial headed 'Biologists in the modern State', *Nature* discussed the results of the survey and said that the supposed excess of supply over demand was to be welcomed. First, because not all of those who qualify are suited to be professional biologists: 'If misfits are to be avoided, it is necessary that more students should read biological subjects than there will be posts available.' Secondly, there was a real need for people who understood biology to work in other fields, particularly as managers and administrators. Finally, the *Nature* editorial suggested, 'in considering how many biologists we require, it is necessary to consider our strategic position if biological warfare should break out', concluding that it would be unwise not to have a reserve of biologists available for emergencies (*Nature*, 1951a). This was written at a time of great apprehension about the intentions of the Soviet Union towards Western Europe and America. We should remember that in June 1950, South Korea had been invaded from the North by forces with Russian support. The invasion was opposed by United Nations forces which had included a small British contingent.

It was widely believed at the time that the Soviet Union was planning to invade Western Europe. In August 1950 the Labour Government had decided upon a massive increase in spending on defence — expenditure that was already running at well over the rates normally seen in times of peace — and compulsory national service was extended to two years. In January 1951, the War Office was predicting that war was 'possible in 1951, probable in 1952', while in February 1951 the Americans completed a series of tests of nuclear weapons in Nevada and were preparing to send a further 100 000 men to support NATO in Europe.

Against this background in March 1950, biological warfare appeared to be a real possibility, but the suggestion that biologists could be employed on biological warfare projects was controversial. It was criticised by a group of biologists at University College London (including G E Fogg, A J Greenbaum, H Gruneberg, J B S Haldane, L S Penrose and A Schweitzer): 'We cannot reconcile ourselves to the use of our biological knowledge, or that which we help students to acquire, for the purposes of destruction,' (*Nature*, 1951b).

Fielding Clarke became involved in the controversy by arranging for reprints of 'Biologists in the modern State' to be sent to Institute of Biology members. However, he had acted without first consulting Council and it was felt that he had exceeded his responsibilities as General Secretary. At a meeting of Council in July 1951 he tendered his resignation. We might note that one of the members of Council in those days went on to play a major role in biological weapons research. As we have seen, R J C Harris, then the Treasurer, was to become Director of the Microbiological Research Establishment at Porton Down 20 years later.

By the next meeting of Council in October, D J B Copp had been appointed General Secretary, with none of the formality that had attended the appointment of his predecessor. Dax Copp was a physicist and was then Assistant Secretary at the British Association. In October 1950 Bob Harris met him at the Institute's conference on *The biological hazards of atomic energy* and suggested that he might like to become the Institute's General Secretary. This he agreed to do, after an interview with Edward Hindle, and stayed with the Institute until 1982. In contrast to the extensive public advertising of the post when Fielding Clarke had been appointed, on this occasion there seems to have been the minimum of consultation.

A few days after the announcement, the Conservatives won the general election of 1951, and Churchill became Prime Minister again at the age of 76.

Changing careers

'Biology as a career' was a topical issue at the time, so the Institute arranged two one-day conferences with this title, to take place in Edinburgh in April 1952 and in Birmingham in October of the same year. There were 10 speakers at the Edinburgh conference, covering, among other things, teaching, fisheries, brewing and university careers. The second conference covered subjects not dealt with in Edinburgh, and was addressed by the Secretaries of the Medical and Agricultural Research Councils, and the Secretary for Colonial Agricultural Research, G A C Herklots (a member of Council). Speakers at both meetings said that employment prospects were better for biologists who also had a knowledge of physics or chemistry.

The first issue of the Institute's booklet *Biology as a Career* was published in 1953 (price to the public, 2/6d or 12.5p). The booklet was edited by Fogg, who became a member of Council in 1952 and succeeded Danielli as Honorary Secretary in 1954. A botanist at University College London, his main research interest was algal physiology. With Michael Abercrombie, he was also joint editor of the Penguin series *New Biology*. These days we can always read current reports in *New Scientist, Scientific American* or *Nature*, or check progress on the Web. Fifty years ago the world of publishing gave us another medium: various series of paperbacks that enabled one to read up on an enormous variety of topics within biology. Some of these series fizzled out after comparatively short runs during the 1960s and early 1970s, but a few persisted into the following decade. Penguin had started it all in 1945 with *New Biology* and *Science News*. The early slim volumes still suffered from wartime restrictions on paper quality and seem relatively primitive by present-day standards. This was a pioneering effort, dating back more than a decade before *New Scientist* first appeared. Few people at that time had access to *Scientific American* and few non-specialists ventured into the specialised papers in *Nature*. Some of the series acquired a very high status indeed and the publishers succeeded in persuading some leading figures in their fields to contribute. Two notable series were American paperbacks, Prentice Hall's *Foundations of Modern Biology* and Addison Wesley's *Principles of Biology*. In the UK Hutchinsons distinguished themselves by producing *Biological Monographs* and publishing many biological texts in their *Home University Library*. An Anglo-American series of over 90 titles attained great popularity. These were the Oxford, later Carolina, *Biology Readers*, characterised by their exceptionally small size (16 or 32 pages), but very authoritatively written. At levels lower than undergraduate similar publishing ventures could be discerned: Longman's *Principles of Modern Biology* produced eight books for sixth-formers while the Hamlyn *All-colour Paperbacks* catered for even younger enthusiasts.

The Institute of Biology was playing an active part of its own. The proceedings of our symposia were published every year from the 1950 volume *The Biological Hazards of Radiation*: was produced in partnership with the Association of Atomic Scientists. The first independent Institute of Biology volume appeared in 1951:

Freezing and Drying, 204 pp, price 14/- (70p). Publication continued throughout the 1960s and beyond, by which time the price of the hardback volumes had increased at first to £1.25 and then in step with increasing production costs. Financial exigencies dictated that the symposia had eventually to be discontinued.

Balancing supply and demand

The Institute was keeping a close watch on the Government's regular surveys of supply and demand in the market for biologists. During the 1950s, the official view of the situation was generally pessimistic. A survey in 1957 showed that demand for biologists was increasing at a lower rate than that for chemists, physicists, geologists or mathematicians. A report in the Institute's *Journal* explained that this was because there was a high proportion (58 per cent) of biologists teaching in schools and technical colleges, where expansion was very small. And in January 1959 Council noted that 'a leaflet prepared by the Ministry of Labour gave the impression to teachers and to parents that the prospects of employment for biologists were not good'.

The *Journal* did find one bright spot in the 1957 survey: 'The report takes no account of the employment of scientists in the Colonies. While this has probably little effect on the figures for other sciences, no picture of the employment of biologists can be complete without the inclusion of figures for graduates of universities in the United Kingdom now working overseas.' At that time, 15 per cent of the Institute's members were in other countries, the largest numbers being in East Africa, Australasia and West Africa.

Biologists abroad

Throughout the 1950s, a significant proportion of biologists who had qualified in Britain were to be found working in the countries of the Commonwealth, the former Colonies and self-governing Dependencies. The Institute encouraged those overseas into membership, and provided such services as it could. In 1955 W Victor Harris was appointed Oversea (sic) Secretary and was co-opted to Council. Harris was an expert on termites, working in Uganda and Tanganyika and at the Natural History Museum. He became Honorary Treasurer and then Vice-President of the Institute in the 1960s. Following a visit to Singapore in 1956, Harris recommended that degrees of the University of Malaya should qualify the holder for membership of the Institute, and this was agreed. A branch of the Institute was set up in Malaya in the following year.

The early issues of the *Journal* carried several general accounts of biological work in countries of the Commonwealth, starting with W H Pearsall on 'Science in East Africa' in the second issue, and covering West Africa, Rhodesia and Nyasaland, the West Indies and Hong Kong. These were rather more than exotica; readers of the

Journal were quite likely to find themselves applying for posts in these countries.

At that time the Government played a major role in supporting scientific work — mainly biological — in Commonwealth countries. There was an Overseas Civil Service, with its own research branch employing scientists overseas. In addition, specialists could be seconded overseas for short-term projects from 'pools' of researchers attached to organisations in the UK. For example, a pool of entomologists was attached to the Commonwealth Institute of Entomology, a few doors from the Institute of Biology's premises in Queen's Gate in Kensington.

In July 1957 the Institute decided to organise a meeting on the professional problems of these biologists in the Colonies. The programme records that the meeting was chaired by 'Kenneth Mellanby, Rothamsted Experimental Station; lately Principal, UC Ibadan, Nigeria'. The costs and complexities of travel in those days were such that speakers were not brought from overseas, but there were plenty of people in Britain who had had recent overseas experience. Of the chairman and five speakers, all but one were 'lately' of a colonial university or research centre. The professional problems that were described at the meeting include the lack of access to library facilities, difficulties of dealing with local administrations, promotion prospects and the problem of obtaining a post on returning home.

The Institute was able to help with the last of these, finding posts for those returning to Britain. From 1952 there had been a service by which vacancies were notified by airmail to overseas members. This must have been the main attraction for members overseas, and repeated appeals for a reduced subscription continued to be turned down because of the Institute's weak financial position.

In 1952, short trips by biologists overseas were being limited by the nation's poor financial showing. The devaluation of the pound coupled with massive expenditure on defence and the new social services caused major economic difficulties. One of the Government's responses was to prohibit private citizens from taking money out of the country. There were special provisions for those travelling abroad on business, including attendances at international conferences. However, those who wanted to go to the Second International Congress of Biochemistry in Paris in July 1952 found it difficult or impossible to get French francs. As President of the Institute, Hindle wrote to the Royal Society to protest, and in due course assurances were received that sufficient foreign currency would be made available in future. However, similar difficulties soon arose in relation to international meetings on microbiology and on physiology. Council discussed the problem several times, and a complaint was made to the Treasury in 1953, after which the situation improved.

Launching the *Journal*

The first issue of the *Journal of the Institute of Biology* was published in November 1953. In 10 pages, it had the things one would expect to find in the journal of a professional society. There was a notice of forthcoming elections to Council, four book reviews, a reminder about those all-important subscriptions, a report on the recent Institute symposium *Biology and productivity of the sea*, and notices of two appointments vacant. This all provided further evidence that the new Institute was working even more actively for the membership.

The most important publication in the first issue was a report on the recent salary survey, which attracted much interest. In those days, there was rather less standardisation of salaries than now, at least in the public sector. The country had been through a period of austerity, and take-home pay was a matter of great concern. The national economic situation had just started to improve. The country was able to export its goods with little competition from others whose industrial bases had suffered greater destruction in the war. The new Conservative Government raised the bank base rate to four per cent in 1952, and the pound continued reasonably stable at $2.80 — in fact it was kept at this level, through thick and thin, until devalued to $2.40 in 1967. Furthermore, by the end of 1953 rationing had virtually ceased. The decision to make a survey of salaries had been made at the first general meeting of the Institute in January 1950. However, the annual general meeting in 1952 agreed that the survey would not be worthwhile until the membership passed the 1000 mark, and it was eventually completed in 1953.

More than half the members of the Institute provided data for the salary survey, the largest groups being those employed in the universities and the civil service. Average annual salaries ranged from under £500 (those aged below 25 in universities) to over £1800 (university staff aged over 51). In this issue of the *Journal*, Birmingham University Medical School was advertising for a PhD biochemist at £650 – £750 pa (currently about £15 000). Virtually everyone was a member of an occupational pension scheme. In all fields except university teaching, the salary scales for women (most of whom were employed in schools and technical colleges) were appreciably lower than those for men.

The *Journal's* book reviews were an important feature. Even in the 1950s there were a lot of American books — sometimes half the reviews were of books from the USA. Most of the reviews were conventional in tone and generally complimentary, but not all. When the first edition of Vines and Rees appeared in 1959 it was severely criticised. The reviewer, A K Thomas, 'reacted immediately against the sheer mass of factual detail' and made a point of including the mass of the two-volume work ('total weight 5.5 lb') in the headline of his review.

Throughout the 1950s there were four issues of the *Journal* each year. It acquired a card cover with the first issue of Volume 2. The first illustration appeared in May 1954 — Ronald Searle's cartoon 'biologists'. There were minor irritations — the biologist who lectured the rest of the membership on how to write English (February 1956) and a light-hearted piece, in May 1959, about what the expressions used in scientific papers really mean ('It has long been known that' means 'I haven't bothered to look it up').

Biologists······ *The celebrated cartoonist Ronald Searle's view of* Biologists, *donated to the Institute and published in the* Journal *in 1954.*

The *Journal's* news coverage was somewhat patchy. There was nothing on the centenary of Darwin's *On the Origin of Species* (1959) except reviews of books that had been issued to mark the occasion. There was no report on the Watson-Crick structure for DNA (1953). In consequence, some members of the Institute were not fully abreast of developments in molecular biology. We can find one example when W B Yapp contributed to the *Journal*. Yapp was a zoologist with a special interest in the ecology of birds, based at Birmingham University. He became a member of Council in 1953, and was Vice-President 1957–59. As late as April 1960 we find Yapp writing in the *Journal* that a gene was 'conceived as a protein or nucleic acid'.

Changes afoot

In its development as a representative institution, the new Institute considered many initiatives, accepting some and declining others. In October 1953 Council rejected the suggestion that there should be distinctive academic dress for Institute members. Similar proposals were considered and rejected several times before the idea was finally accepted in 1979.

The Institute's second major conference on *Careers in biology* was held in Edinburgh in 1952. The organisation of the event brought together biologists in Scotland, and led to the formation of the first of the Institute's Branches. Those for London and the Midlands were set up in 1953, and there is now a comprehensive network covering the United Kingdom (see Appendix). In 1957 Council agreed to the formation of a Branch in Ireland, on representations of nine members meeting in Dublin. In the following year the General Secretary visited Belfast, and Council agreed to the formation of a Branch for Northern Ireland. The Irish Branch was dissolved when the Institute of Biology of Ireland was formed in 1965.

When Hindle retired as the Institute's first President in 1953, he was succeeded by F E Fritsch. Fritsch had been Head of the department of botany at Queen Mary College, London, since the department was created in 1911, and was the author of the widely used *Structure and Reproduction of the Algae*. Unfortunately, he died the very next year and was succeeded as President by Sir James Gray, who had been Professor of Zoology in Cambridge University since 1937. Gray's principal research interests were cytology and animal locomotion.

In 1954 it was suggested that there should be a National Certificate in Biology, similar to the National Certificate in Chemistry then widely taught in technical colleges. The suggestion was made by I A Preece, an expert on fermentation at what was then Edinburgh's Heriot-Watt College. He was a member of the committee on biology in technical colleges set up by Council later that year. At that time, technical colleges offered GCE Ordinary and Advanced level courses in biological subjects and, in some cases, external degrees of the University of London. The Institute tried to persuade the Government that there should be a scheme of National Certificates in Biology. The Government seemed sympathetic, but in the event was not persuaded. Instead the Institute established a scheme by which certificates awarded by the colleges were endorsed by the Institute, with the Institute undertaking responsibility for approving the courses and appointing external assessors for examinations set by the colleges. The Ministry of Education declined invitations to endorse the certificates jointly with the Institute, but the certificates were accepted by major employers such as the Medical Research Council and the Civil Service Commission. The scheme was eventually taken on board by the Ministry of Education in the early 1960s.

In 1957 Gray retired as President and was succeeded by W H Pearsall, Professor of Botany at University College London. A plant ecologist with a special interest in freshwater ecology and moorlands, he was the author of *Mountains and Moorlands*.

The new Institute had always had something of an industrial relations organisation about it, and was frequently involved with issues of employment, such as terms and conditions of service. As we have seen, this was laid down at the outset, when one of the proposed functions of the Institute was 'to protect the standards of employment of its members, if need be by providing legal aid'. As early as the first general meeting in January 1950 it had been agreed that there should be a salary census. In presenting this proposal on behalf of the Council, T A Bennet-Clark pointed out that, although a professional institute was prevented by the terms of its charter from acting as a trade union, 'it was not debarred, however, from taking an interest in the financial as well as the professional well-being of its members'. He pointed out that the Institutes representing the chemists and physicists had already made similar surveys of salaries. Bennet-Clark (1903–75) was a plant physiologist who held chairs in Nottingham, King's College London, and the University of East Anglia. He was a member of the original Provisional Council, and Vice-President of the Institute 1954–55.

Should we be a trade union?

The general policy that the Institute of Biology is a professional institute rather than a trade union was maintained fairly consistently throughout the 50 years from the Institute's inception until the present day. However, there were many proposals to change that policy, particularly in the early days. One of the results of the great statutory exercises in industrial relations of the 1970s and 1980s was a clear legal definition of a trade union. Today there is a clearer understanding of what is, and what is not, a union.

In the 1950s matters were not so clearly defined, and it was possible for members to hold a wide variety of opinions about what, if anything, the Institute should do by way of activity on behalf of working members. Many believed that the Institute should not involve itself in trade union work, concentrating instead on representing the interests of biologists only as part of the broad programme to advance biology itself. On the other hand, many believed that the Institute should take on a more active representational role, defending or promoting the interests of individuals or groups of members. It was possible for members to hold opposing views because it had never been decided where the Institute stood on the matter. Thus, when invited to become a member in 1952, Sir Edward Salisbury declined because there seemed to be no safeguard against the Institute engaging in political activities.

The debate continued with greater or lesser intensity throughout the early years, and came to a head in the mid-1950s. A committee on professional matters was set up in 1955, and in March 1956 recommended the continuation of the policy of being 'not a trade union'. However, at that time members were raising a succession of issues with a trade-union flavour for Council to consider. They included the need for a survey of members' satisfaction with the established trade unions (the Association of Scientific Workers, the Association of University Teachers, and the Institution of Professional Civil Servants), the conditions of service of those transferred to the employment of the new Agricultural Research Council (ARC), posts for biologists advertised at 'too low a salary', and so on.

Some of the issues raised could affect a large number of people. For example, in 1955 Derek Minter was a postgraduate student at the London School of Hygiene and Tropical Medicine (LSHTM), supported by a grant from the Medical Research Council (MRC). The Ministry of Pensions and National Insurance interviewed him and decided that he was self-employed, and so liable to pay National Insurance contributions at self-employed rates. The reasoning seems to have been that postgraduates were carrying out research, rather than being trained in the methods of research, and so were gainfully employed. At that stage Minter owed almost £30 in back contributions, a large sum of money for a postgraduate student in those days, though the authorities agreed not to enforce payment in his case. He appealed for help to the Institute, which took up the matter with the Ministry and the MRC, and enlisted the support of the Institute of Physics and the Royal Institute of Chemistry.

It is interesting to note that, after leaving the LSHTM, Minter decided on a career change. Perhaps because of all this exposure to financial affairs, he left biology and went to work in financial services.

In 1957 the country was plunged into political crisis following the dispute over the Suez Canal. In January Anthony Eden resigned as Prime Minister and was succeeded by Harold Macmillan. During that year the Institute held its eighth annual general meeting at University College London. There was a discussion on future policy, and several members said that the Institute should (as the minutes record) take 'a greater interest in professional matters'. These representations were considered at the next meeting of Council, which had before it a memorandum prepared by T C Carter. Carter had been very active in the Institute from the outset. A founder member, he had been present at the first general meeting (when Bennet-Clark had said that the Institute would not act as a trade union) and had attended the 1957 AGM. He had contributed a paper on the induction of mutations to the Institute's conference *The biological hazards of atomic energy* in 1950. In 1957 he was working for the MRC at Harwell. In due course he was to become Head of Genetics at the MRC Radiobiology Research Unit at Harwell, and eventually Director of the Poultry Research Centre in Edinburgh.

Carter's memorandum said that he was not eligible to join the Association of University Teachers (AUT) or the Institution of Professional Civil Servants (IPCS), being neither a university teacher nor a civil servant. He did not want to join the only other trade union that then organised a substantial number of scientists, the Association of Scientific Workers (AScW), because of sensitivities about work at Harwell. He goes on: 'Apart from the Institute of Biology, I therefore have no professional body to represent my interests in discussions with my employer. The need for such a body is perhaps especially obvious to a biologist employed by the MRC, since he is working alongside others who have a powerful professional body behind them, the British Medical Association.'

Carter details some specific points on which he would like support from the Institute, and makes it clear that this kind of support is the *only* service that he wants from the Institute. The question of the Institute's proper role in these matters was discussed by the professional matters committee, and in due course Council agreed to pursue some of the specific points that Carter had raised — for example, an approach to the MRC and the ARC to ask that salaries of their staffs be published in the same way as those of civil servants. No moves were made to take an active role as a trade union. Carter was made one of the Institute representatives on the Joint Council of Professional Scientists, and in January 1958 he became Secretary of the professional matters committee.

At this time questions began to be asked about the numbers of biologists who were members of trade unions. A survey was carried out and the results were published in the *Journal* in 1959. In the universities, schools and technical colleges, the scientific civil service and the Atomic Energy Authority, it was estimated that between 50 and 80 per cent of employed biologists were members of the appropriate trade union (then described as 'staff associations'). However, there was no recognised union for the ARC, though about 10 per cent of the eligible staff of ARC establishments were members of the AScW. In practice, ARC salaries and conditions of service were always based on those of the civil service, negotiated by the IPCS. Accordingly the Institute proposed that ARC staff should be eligible to join the IPCS. This brought a protest from John Dutton, AScW General Secretary, who said that there was a long-standing agreement with the IPCS that they would not seek to organise ARC staff. Furthermore, the ARC did recognise the AScW as authorised to represent the interests of those ARC staff in membership of the AScW. Five years later the IPCS decided that it would recruit ARC staff.

The objective of the survey of biologists' membership of trade unions is not entirely clear. There seems to have been a feeling that the Institute should not, or need not, involve itself in trade union activities so long as other organisations were representing biologists adequately. The matter was finally resolved in 1971 when the Industrial Relations Act required any organisation carrying on the functions of a trade union to register with a Government-appointed registrar. The ASTMS (successor to the AScW, and now MSF), the AUT, the IPCS (now the IPMS) and the BMA all registered as trade unions. The Institute of Biology did not.

Improving the status of biology

Although the institutions representing biologists, chemists and physicists often worked together, biologists sometimes found themselves with special problems of their own. In 1957, men aged 18 were still required to do national service, but in that year it was agreed that those with a first-class honours degree in science should have indefinite deferment. However, Institute members with first-class honours degrees were astonished to find that local offices still did not officially regard biological subjects as 'science', and the matter was only resolved when the Institute made representations to the Government. Again, in 1957 it was found that a Government fund for the advancement of science education was making grants to schools to build laboratories for chemistry and physics, but not for biology. This was said to be because industrial demand was mainly for chemists and physicists, and in this case the Institute was unable to change official policy.

As the 1950s drew to a close, the Institute was in good shape. In 1959 Pearsall retired as President and was replaced by Sir Alan Parkes. An expert on reproductive physiology, Parkes was then head of the Division of Experimental Biology at the National Institute for Medical Research at Mill Hill, north London. He had graduated in agriculture at Cambridge and worked at University College London. In 1961 he became Professor of the Physiology of Reproduction at Cambridge. Of the three people who had managed the Institute in the early years, Hindle and Danielli no longer held office, though Bob Harris was now one of the four Vice-Presidents.

In 1959 the Institute had a total membership of 2231 and this was steadily increasing at about 10 per cent per annum. Once the lease had been taken for the fifth floor at 41 Queen's Gate, an Assistant was appointed to work with the General Secretary. There had been an excess of income over expenditure for the year of £196, and there was over £200 in the bank. There was great activity amongst the nine Branches. Ten colleges were teaching the Institute's Endorsed Certificates in Biology. The *Journal* was redesigned and expanded ready for Volume 7, published in January 1960.

British biology was in good shape too. Even though the Institute was not involved in organising them, there had been many celebrations for the centenary of the publication of *On the Origin of Species* in 1859. A succession of British discoveries had made the headlines in the 1950s, of which the most celebrated had been the Watson and Crick structure for DNA in 1953. Biology was becoming more visible to the general public, although, sadly, the popular series *New Biology* (published by Penguin) was closing. In the autumn of 1959, the BBC's Reith Lectures were being given by Peter Medawar, Professor of Zoology and Comparative Anatomy at University College London, who was to receive the Nobel Prize for Physiology or Medicine in the following year. Michael Swann, Professor of Natural History at the University of Edinburgh, appeared on the front cover of the *Radio Times* posing with a microscope to promote the television programme *What is Life?*, transmitted on the evening of 2 December 1959.

In 10 years, both biology and the Institute of Biology had made a great deal of progress.

References

Danielli J F (1948) A proposed Institute of Biology. *Nature,* **162,** 878.

Nature (1951a) Biologists in the modern State. *Nature,* **167,** 371-372.

Nature (1951b) Biologists in the modern State. *Nature,* **167,** 660.

A COMMITTEE CHAIRMAN REFLECTS

David R Morgan CBiol FIBiol
Chairman, Biomedical Sciences Committee 1996–99

❝ Shortly after joining the Institute in the early 1980s, I attended a meeting of the biomedical sciences committee and was warmly welcomed into the fold. There were some delightful characters on the committee, including the late Stuart Roath, a medical man; Diana Anderson, a distinguished toxicologist; and Alan Johnston, chemist, biologist, wine expert, and much more — all three were to take a key role in the Institute's biomedical affairs by chairing the committee over the next 10 years.

I also had an earlier spell on the old-style Council, with lots of members, in 1992. One may have thought this was recognition for organising a successful national conference, but I fear it was more likely a response to a suggestion that Council could benefit from the participation of one or two 'younger faces'. The benefit was that I was able to meet senior and distinguished colleagues by the roomful and observe at first hand how business was done. It was also a unique opportunity to meet a series of Presidents and to observe the particular ways whereby they would influence the course of discussion and decision-making. A sense of humour always helps. Positive reflection comes easily when contemplating *all* the Past-Presidents over the last 12 years, a period when sustained growth and development was clearly experienced by the Institute. I can easily say that we were fortunate to have such effective and pleasant personalities at the top of the organisation — and this continues to the present day. Humour, Chinese proverbs, and wise counsel were in abundance. There were also unforgettable characters among the ordinary members of Council at that time; the oratory and eloquence of Brian J Ford immediately spring to mind.

If my association with the Institute of Biology has been pleasant and warming, equally it has been professionally rewarding and challenging. The successful conference mentioned earlier was a timely response to the AIDS epidemic, *AIDS: a challenge in education* (1989), and resulted in a half-full auditorium (over 500 delegates) at the London University Institute of Education. Organisation and financial responsibilities for the event were awesome and driven by enthusiasm of the few. Conferences organised by Institute committees are not given executive committee blessing easily. Success depended, as it did over my full term of office, on some key individuals — and the most key was Jonathan Cowie. This conference, with an array of notable AIDS experts, a huge turnout and financially successful exhibition, helped to put biomedicine on the Institute's map. The subsequent proceedings that I edited and published jointly with the Royal Society of Medicine further convinced us of the value of this sort of initiative.

Our conferences *Managing biological and chemical risks: a strategy for working in biomedical, laboratory and clinical environments* (1995), run in conjunction with the Wellcome Trust, and *Are natural therapies safe and effective?* (1997), held at the Royal Pharmaceutical Society, extended the Institute's influence into further important fields of biology and medicine. They also made a profit. The next conference *The biology of air pollution*, of October 1999, a two-day meeting with an array of internationally known names on the speakers' list, must have equalled anything put on by the Royal Society or medical Royal Colleges. The brainchild of Terry Tetley of the British Association for Lung Research, this meeting had been nurtured through endless Science Board, Affiliated Societies Forum, and finance committee meetings, where Tetley used great charm and persuasion to generate support.

If the Institute has enjoyed leadership from a succession of very fitting Presidents, in the same way holders of the post of General Secretary have made their mark: the purchase of the new building, the big reorganisation of the committees, the new coat of arms, recruitment challenges, financial crises, and many other matters have been tackled, not always as quickly as some would wish, but with a successful outcome in the main. The appointment of a Chief Executive creates further opportunities for the post holder to innovate, develop, and manage change, and Alan Malcolm has yet to get into third gear. The speed of development in the next few years is likely to surprise us all.

The power of the Institute's voice has become much louder over the years, enhanced by the 70 or so specialised learned societies affiliated to the Institute. As a professional body we are now regular contributors to Government consultation exercises on a vast range of issues — we must be clear, however, that on some occasions we may have some problems in supporting the Government line. The Institute view must be authoritative and balanced, but also shed new light on areas of concern, particularly if the wider environment or human health is at stake.

As Brian Ford commented in closing the memorable biomedical sciences conference on *Biological and chemical risks:* 'It is not the unanswered questions which bedevil us … but those that have yet to be asked.' I am indebted to the Institute for providing endless hours of stimulation, entertainment and learning over the years. Although not quite a biologists' club, it has great potential and could, in the next 50 years or so, surely become one. **99**

EXAMINING THE SIXTIES

Bernard Thomason PhD CBiol MIBiol

*Honorary Archivist, Institute of Biology, and former Senior Lecturer
in Biology, Manchester Metropolitan University*

The folk memory of the 1960s is that of a period of optimism and change. In popular culture we had the new E-type Jaguar, while British bands like the Beatles and the Rolling Stones held a dominant role in the American phenomenon of 'flower power'. At the Institute the scene was also one of change and, in particular, educational reform. Clearly this was timely; by the end of the decade we were to see students in open revolt. As a student member at the time I well recall the first meeting that I attended. It was the inaugural meeting of the North Wales Branch in May 1964, and much interest centred on the address given by J Heslop-Harrison on *The changing pattern of biology teaching*. As the Institute's *Journal* for August 1964 reported, it 'aroused interest and stimulated active discussion'.

Making up for lost time

The biology student in 1960 was faced with a curriculum and with laboratory exercises that had not changed much over 60 or 70 years. The majority of A-level students found that biology was yet to appear as a single subject; the disciplines were largely taught separately as botany and zoology. Those studying botany in 1960 would have felt completely at home with the scope and content of W Gardiner's syllabus of *A Course of Practical Botany* (Gardiner, 1890). But changes to the traditional botany and zoology courses were beginning to take place and a number of universities had their courses outlined in the *Journal*. These included major bodies which had just become, or were soon to become, universities: East Anglia, Brunel, Sussex and Bath, as well as recently established universities such as Keele and Leicester. Most described the formation of schools of biology, which were seen as a way of promoting teaching and research in branches of biology that cut across the old disciplinary boundaries. Such developments were given great impetus by a Royal Society report to the Government advisory committee on scientific policy, published in 1961. A good deal of support for the movement towards greater integration and co-ordination of undergraduate courses was similarly expressed at a meeting of British botany professors held at Bedford College in March 1964. It was at this meeting that W O James explained the aims of the new biological education committee, set up jointly by the Royal Society and the Institute, with a crucial brief: to consider the improvement of biological teaching and make recommendations for action.

Biological education in schools was much influenced by the work of the Science

Masters' Association (SMA) and the Association of Women Science Teachers (AWST), which amalgamated in 1963 to form the Association for Science Education. By 1961, the SMA and AWST had formulated proposals for modernising science courses on a national scale, but financial help was required. Eventually the necessary assistance was secured from the Nuffield Foundation, and details of the Nuffield Foundation Science Teaching Project were first publicly announced in the House of Commons in April 1962 by the Minister of Education, Sir David Eccles. W H Dowdeswell, one of our Vice-Presidents during the 1960s, was appointed organiser of the Foundation's Biology Project. Subsequently, new examination schemes were introduced which included O- and A-level biology. The schemes emphasised enquiry and they involved a large amount of practical work. The courses set out every need in detail and tended to be all-or-nothing courses that were hard to encompass piecemeal. Many enthusiastically flew the flags of enquiry and the development of novel practical work. The Nuffield schemes, even if not adopted universally, were a potent influence on all engaged in developing school science.

The Institute, through the biological education committee, brought its own influence to bear in a number of ways. A two-year survey was carried out for the biological education committee to give a comprehensive and reliable picture of biological education in the UK. Financed by a grant from the Nuffield Foundation, the resulting report *Biology in Sixth Forms and Universities* appeared in 1967. The more important findings were that numbers of pupils studying biology had been increasing by about 13 per cent per annum, and changing syllabuses — reflecting important developments in the subject — would make new demands and require provision of in-service training for teachers. Meanwhile, the inadequate supply of laboratory technical staff was going to prove to be a limiting factor, for the majority of university departments preferred entrants having competence in the physical sciences as well as biology.

The biological education committee had produced a report in 1966 on the supply of biological materials. It concluded that the situation was poor in schools, less pressing in technical and training colleges, and created least anxiety in universities. Focusing on the pressing needs of school biology, especially in the light of the Nuffield Biology Project, the report aired various proposals for the supply of a wide-ranging selection of organisms. The committee applied for a grant to the Schools Council and it agreed to provide £7000 per annum for three years from April 1969 to establish a development unit for living material. The unit was housed at the Centre for Science Education at Chelsea College and a research fellow was appointed from September 1969. Further work of the biological education committee was reported in the *Journal* for May 1969. The committee 'was likely to receive a grant from the DES to support centres for biology teachers in some 10 or a dozen universities'. The vision was that such centres would be open for teachers on specified evenings to share facilities for experimental work, and to see new equipment and organisms with potential for teaching purposes. Each centre would have a steering committee drawn from university personnel, LEA staff, science inspectors and teachers. The Institute had long recognised this need and, indeed, our *Journal* had published lists of short courses for biology teachers since the decade began.

To complement its interest in the development of biological education, the Institute next proposed to set up an investigation of the requirements of major employers of biologists. It was hoped that this would provide information for universities and colleges of technology to consider the expansion of numbers in certain existing courses or the introduction of new courses. An application was submitted to the DES for a grant in aid of the proposed investigation and in February 1966 the Department agreed to finance a report. The result was *A Survey of the Employment of Graduates in Biological Posts in the UK*, and it was published in the *Journal* in November 1966.

The information that had been gathered countered the widespread opinion that posts available to science graduates were restricted to those in chemistry, physics and engineering. Dax Copp pointed out in *Biologist* (Copp, 1971) that for its first 15 years (until about 1965) the Institute corrected the commonly held view, especially among headmasters, that 'there is little future outside teaching for those with a biological degree'. At the time, more than 11 000 graduates were employed in biology, the largest single group of 4000 being employed as teachers, mainly in the secondary schools. Here most of the teaching was of broad-based, general biology. In the remaining fields of employment — universities, state-aided research and industry — the emphasis was increasingly on specialisation. There was a strong demand from state-aided research and the universities for disciplines such as plant physiology and pathology, agronomy/horticulture, animal physiology and entomology. In comparison, the biological posts in industry tended to demand biochemistry, microbiology, pharmacology, toxicology and immunology. There was no strict relationship between the subjects chosen for university training and the student's subsequent employment, but increases in those trained in microbiology and biochemistry would clearly be timely. However, 40 per cent of graduate biologists would become teachers, mainly of general biology, so for this, among other reasons, a basic training in this subject remained a priority.

As changes were occurring in biology in the universities, so the Institute expanded its own role in higher and further education. Copp recalls how, in the 1950s, the Institute had worked for the introduction by a number of technical colleges of certificates in biology along the lines of the National Certificate in Chemistry. Awarded by the colleges, certificates were endorsed by the signature of the Institute's President, the Institute having approved the courses and appointed external assessors. By 1960 the Scottish Education Department agreed to establish with the Institute a joint committee for National Certificates in Biology, and then in 1962 the

Ministry of Education joined the Institute in a scheme for a Higher National Certificate in Applied Biology. Two years later, the Ordinary Endorsed Certificate was absorbed into a comprehensive scheme for an Ordinary National Certificate in Sciences with Institute representation on its joint committee. We must remember that, until these developments, biology in technical colleges had been largely restricted to GCE O- and A-levels and external degrees of London University, so these initiatives gave the Institute a prominent role as an assessor of students of biology.

Admission by examination

At the Institute AGM in January 1964, a by-law was passed to admit persons to membership by examination. A prime mover in this development was the President, G E Blackman. It would extend the opportunity for higher education in biology, and it was envisaged that the examination would be taken after three years' part-time study by persons entering the course with a Higher National Certificate (HNC) in Applied Biology. There would be a Part 1 membership examination at the end of the first year, at which papers would be taken in the principles of biology and in a special subject. The Part 2 examination would be on the special subject alone. In 1964, subjects under consideration were biochemistry, entomology, microbiology, pharmacology and plant pathology. By May 1964, some 20 technical colleges were hoping to offer courses with an intake of about 150 students. By November 1964, Council had approved the examination structure and courses that were expected to begin in September 1965. The first examinations for the HNC in Applied Biology were held in 1964 at 12 colleges in England and Wales, with two in Scotland.

A year later the Institute's AGM passed revised by-laws to replace the non-corporate grade of Associate Member with the corporate grade of Licentiate. Qualifications required for the new grade would be the possession of a degree, passing of Part 1 of the membership examination, or an equivalent qualification. Full membership would usually be attained by passing both parts of the membership examination or possessing a first- or second-class degree followed by three years of 'responsible experience'. These changes, it was argued, would bring membership requirements into line with those of the Institutes of Chemistry and Physics. By 1968, membership examinations were well established at a number of colleges across the country (Part 1 in 16, Part 2 in 10). Biochemistry, followed by microbiology, were the most popular special options. Most students attended on a day- or block-release system. In February 1967 the largest proportion of students (60 per cent) came from industrial organisations, followed by 12 per cent from the Medical Research Council and 10 per cent from hospitals, universities, and colleges. The remainder came from Government departments, the Agricultural Research Council and local authorities. Some four per cent of the students attended full time. It was also in 1968 that Council decided to introduce new regulations relating to those entering membership on the strength of a dissertation. Such persons would be required to have passed the Part 1 membership examination or to have a pass or third-class honours degree.

While an HNC in Applied Biology remained the normal entry requirement for the membership examination, in 1969 Council started to accept for entry those with an HNC in medical laboratory subjects or a Teacher's Certificate where biology was the main subject. The membership examination rapidly gained recognition as the equivalent of a full degree. It was soon recognised by universities as an entry quali-fication for higher degrees. By 1968 it was recognised as a graduate equivalent for teachers, and this was quickly followed by the Civil Service Commission which accepted the membership examination for entry to the Scientific Officer grade. The Medical Research Council and the National Agricultural Advisory Service gave sim-ilar recognition. R J Terry, writing in the *Journal* (Terry, 1968), noted the high stan-dard of the examination and that the expected output at Part 2 was to be between 70 and 100 trained and experienced biologists per year. A new subject, ecology and behaviour, had been designed especially for those teaching biology in schools who did not possess first- or second-class honours degrees.

The communication revolution

There were many other valuable initiatives in biological education by the Institute during the decade. A conference was held in April 1965 on the production and use of films in biology teaching. This resulted in the setting up of a films committee to encourage the making of teaching films which could be made readily available to teachers. The bio-logical education committee inaugurated the valuable series of booklets, *Studies in Biology,* which first became available in 1966, pro-duced by Edward Arnold Ltd in conjunc-tion with the Institute. In 1965 it was announced that a *Biology Teachers' Handbook* would be published in the fol-lowing year. This would provide 'practi-cal information to help with everyday work'. By Easter 1967 we saw the launch of the *Journal of Biological*

A typical cover of the first series of Studies in Biology, the 1970 reprint of first study Ecological Energetics *by John Phillipson (first edition 1966).*

Changes in design since the
Journal of Biological
Education
was launched in 1967

Education, the editorial policy for which the Institute was responsible through an editorial board. The commitment of the Institute to educational activities had been further advanced in 1965 by the appointment of an Education Officer. A leading figure in the educational work of the Institute from the beginning of the decade was O E Lowenstein, who served as President 1965–66. In addition to the work of Institute headquarters, the regions also organised meetings on educational topics; for example, the Western Branch held an exhibition on *Biology in schools* in November 1965.

A major theme addressed by the Institute during the 1960s was communication in biology. Bradford Institute of Technology (now Bradford University) had pioneered a course on the use of biological literature. This first took place over two days in October 1964. It was held annually for several years thereafter, and in the *Journal* Bottle and Wyatt (1965) provided a brief description of the course. In December 1966 the Institute held a conference and exhibition on the subject. The report in the *Journal* of February 1967 included a list of agreed recommendations. These dealt with such issues as clarity, the avoidance of multiple publication, quoting only essential references, and links between UK abstracting systems and information-retrieval organisations and those in other countries. Copp (1971) remarked that the report 'provided working biologists both with a useful conspectus of the problems of communication and advice from specialists on the techniques of information retrieval, the writing of papers and the citing of references'. It was also recommended that Council should approach ASLIB and the Biological Council with proposals for a committee on biological information which would be representative of major groups of biologists, editors and information scientists. One of its functions would be to provide a forum for discussion by biologists and those specialising in information work. In September 1969, the new biological information committee organised a workshop for lecturers about recent developments.

In the columns of the *Journal* between August 1964 and November 1966, lists of new words and their meanings were published in order to elicit comment prior to inclusion in a proposed Biological Council *Dictionary of Specialist Terms*. Elsewhere in the *Journal*, worries were being expressed about the flood of new words that were deluging scientists (see, for example, the issue of May 1967, page 53). One anonymous writer suggested that this problem could be lessened if the number of new papers published was to be reduced. To achieve this, it was suggested that parallel publication in more than one journal should be prevented and that there should be stricter refereeing.

Discussion about communication in the broadest sense was enlivened by a number of papers published in our *Journal* during the decade. One contributor, (Despopoulos, 1964), advised on 'How to get the most out of scientific literature'. When confronted with a large volume of papers, his advice was to scan both ends of each paper, disregarding text that lay between title and bibliography. From this, he maintained, it should be possible to make an informed estimate of how much time should be spent reading the text. Many of us have not forgotten his advice! Despopoulos made many amusing observations. Here is an example: 'Valuable inferences can also be drawn from the list of references ... Some authors fill their bibliographies only with their own earlier publications. This is done principally when the author feels that he has not been quoted sufficiently by other writers.' Again: 'This has the further effect of suggesting that no one else is capable of contributing useful ideas to that particular problem.' A second amusing and useful article by P C Williams appeared in the following year (Williams, 1965a), with 'Suggestions for speakers and standards for slides'. It provided many valuable and hard-hitting suggestions, among which was: 'Don't speak to the desk or the slides ... The back of your head may look nicer than your face but the audience are there to hear what you have to say.' He added: 'Speakers going beyond the allotted time show themselves to be conceited, incompetent and ill-mannered.' Clearly, the Institute was being seen increasingly as an arbiter of standards in biology, and authors expressed themselves with wit and style.

Council first set up a public relations committee in 1965, under the chairmanship of H O J Collier, to make more widely appreciated the work of the Institute and the social value of the science it represented. Members of the Institute were encouraged to come forward with ideas and offers of help to speed the work of improving the public image of biology. Concerns emerging then seem even more relevant now. Several contributors addressed the issue in the *Journal*'s columns. Hutchinson (1965) was concerned that inaccurate ideas and images about biology needed to be corrected. This required more than increased publicity for the material benefits which biological research provided. He considered these benefits to be too much part of daily life to excite much feeling. They lacked the touch of mystery which so many had learned to attribute to 'real' science. He believed that some educational approaches tended to equate 'science' with 'giving information about the results of scientific enquiries, and practising techniques'. Such approaches did not stress the sorts of thinking that were involved in the enquiries. This led to the idea that the most scientific and intellectually rewarding subjects were those which use the most complex apparatus to study the most narrowly defined problems.

One answer, according to Price Jones (1967), was to communicate effectively in the popular press rather than merely 'whispering in a scientific journal'. First, biologists should write 'clearly, succinctly, and in a reasonably interesting manner' and secondly, 'research stations and university departments should cultivate a more benign attitude towards publication in the popular press'. Brian (1968) made some observations on the Dainton report. While applauding the report's recommendations for science education in schools, Brian argued that what was also needed was a change in the public estimation of science. Existing publicity failed to put across what individual scientists really felt to be the value of science and the scientific approach. It failed to 'communicate … the variety of motivations which impel us', and failed to show 'why even in this imperfect world we like being scientists'. He advocated giving young people a glimpse of why intellectual rigour is necessary in science, and that logic and precision in thought still leaves room for imagination, intellectual adventure and social responsibility.

A notable feature of the communication of the decade was the annual symposium, which was often reported in the public media. Topics were diverse, for example *The biology of space travel* (1960), *Exploitation of the world's fauna for food* (1961), *The biological significance of climatic changes in Britain* (1964), *Man-made lakes* (1965), *Biology and the manufacturing industries* (1966), *Problems of birds as pests* (1967), and *Biology and ethics* (1968). The last symposium of the decade was on *The optimum population for Britain* (1969). This received considerable press and radio reporting and we had five Members of Parliament in the audience.

Responding to the times

Throughout the 1960s conservation and environmental issues were becoming widely aired. Copp (1971) asserted that the Institute symposia made a contribution to public awareness of such issues. Indeed, he remarked that the Institute acted as 'foster parent to the Council for Nature as a means of bringing together all those concerned with nature conservation to provide a more effective public pressure group'. For its first eight years, the Council for Nature staff shared the Institute's premises and Copp acted as its part-time General Secretary. In 1966 they obtained new premises at the Zoological Society in Regent's Park.

Another annual event was the Darwin Lecture in Human Biology. This was inaugurated by the President, Sir Gerard Thornton, in 1960 with support from the Eugenics Society. The first lecture was given by C E Ford in November 1960 on *Cytogenetics of sex in man*. Thornton also paved the way for the decision in 1963 to introduce Fellowships. This brought the Institute into line with its sister institutes, although in earlier years the grade of Fellow had been considered unnecessary and pretentious.

Another aspect of the Institute's activities was its developing involvement in responding to Government committees. In 1963, a committee was set up under the chairmanship of Sir Sydney Littlewood 'to consider the present control over experiments on living animals, and to consider whether, and if so what, changes are desirable in the law or its administration'. The Littlewood report was published in April 1965. It was proposed that many of the report's recommendations should form the basis of the new legislation. This would effectively replace the Cruelty to Animals Act 1876. In general, many of those biologists whose work would be affected by the proposals saw them in terms of increasing bureaucracy with few attendant advantages. P C Williams (1965b), then the Honorary Secretary of the Biological Council, concluded: 'If the Littlewood report does form the basis of a new Act the lawyers and bureaucrats may benefit but the biologist will suffer and the laboratory animal will be no better off than he is at present.' Council of the Institute responded to the report by sending a statement to the Home Secretary, reported in the *Journal* of February 1966 (pages 17 – 20). The statement drew specific attention to those recommendations which could lead to major difficulties and concluded that an Act based on the report 'would lead to serious difficulties and greatly impede biological research on animals, without providing any real benefit for the experimental animals'.

Our President in 1967 was H J Bunker, who had considerable firsthand experience of the Civil Service, so it seems fitting that in that year the Institute submitted a memorandum to the Fulton Commission on the Civil Service. The memorandum dealt first 'with the improvement of the efficiency of the Civil Service by changes in the status of the scientist in general and biologist in particular and in the organisation of the Civil Service, especially at higher levels'. Underlying its suggestions was the timely concern that scientifically qualified persons were almost totally absent from administrative and executive classes and that science specialists were subordinate to non-technical administrators. The second part of the memorandum was concerned with modifications to Scientific Civil Service structure 'designed to increase efficiency in the use of biologists and to offer satisfactory careers'. Those comments have remained pertinent in the years that have followed. As well as its response to official committees and Royal Commissions, the Institute also responded to specific Government actions. Copp has described how, in 1962, the Institute wrote to the Treasury 'to express concern that the grants to universities to be made by Government were lower than the scale proposed by the University Grants Committee'. Other bodies made similar protests with the result that university expansion was not, at the time, adversely affected. Employment issues have, of course, always been a concern of the Institute.

Overseas development

Both H J Bunker and his successor as President, F C Bawden, were personally active in encouraging research overseas, and the Institute in the last years of the decade looked into overseas development. In 1967 the Institute organised a meeting between senior biologists with overseas experience and representatives of bodies employing biologists overseas, including the Ministry of Overseas Development. The meeting was called in view of overseas employment becoming increasingly beset by problems arising from the political and social changes taking place in Africa and elsewhere during the decade. It was generally agreed that, although it was seldom possible for biologists to make a full career abroad, a period of overseas experience would be valuable. Furthermore, the Institute had a role to play in encouraging overseas service by biologists. As a result of the meeting, Council constituted an overseas service committee of members with experience of working as biologists abroad. Its role would be to advise Council on policy matters and, in due course, provide services for those overseas and those considering overseas postings. One of the committee's first tasks was to ask British employers what they felt about the value of overseas experience. The findings indicated that no biologist contemplating return from overseas would be rejected out of hand by any would-be employer. There was a general belief that overseas experience increased the value of prospective employees, although this was countered by a feeling by some employers that returning expatriates might not always be of first-class academic stature. The overall conclusion was that overseas biologists may expect to have their records and qualifications subjected to particularly careful scrutiny but, having been accepted for a post, could hope to be given equal status to other employees of equal age and experience in the UK.

By April 1968 the Scientists' Appointments Service (SAS) had been set up by the five science and technology institutes that, in February 1969, became the Council of Science and Technology Institutes. The principal object of the SAS was to facilitate the return to employment in the UK of British scientists and technologists who had been working abroad. It was appreciated that the work of the SAS would be difficult since industrial recruitment in the UK had already been running at a low level.

There had been a slowing down of recruitment by universities, colleges and Government research establishments, and yet there had been an increased output of scientists and technologists from the growing number of universities. Nevertheless, by May 1969, scientists and technologists registered with the SAS numbered about 800, with about 100 employers (nearly all industrial companies) also registered with the scheme.

In 1961 and again in 1969 a survey was made of advertisements for graduate biologists appearing in *Nature*. A comparison of the surveys shows that there was an increase from 163 to 351 in overseas university posts. At home, university posts rose from 158 to 528, research posts from 171 to 562, and appointments in industry from 87 to 232. Account was not taken of teaching posts in schools and colleges of education, of which 1300 were notified to the *Times Educational Supplement* in 1962. Overall, comparison shows a broad correspondence between the rates of increase in output and demand. The demand for specialists was high, especially in microbiology and biochemistry, although for biology teachers in schools a course in general biology, botany or zoology remained the appropriate subject qualification. Demand for microbiologists by the end of the decade contrasted markedly with the state of affairs 10 years earlier. John Postgate was Secretary of a working party set up in 1960–61 by the learned societies (including the Institute) to report on the state of UK research in economic microbiology.

He recalls: 'Naturally it found the state of the subject lamentable, and recommended the civilianisation of the Military Research Establishment, the Biological Warfare Station at Porton, with a remit to add economic microbiology to its programme. The report reached the Minister of Science, was endorsed by the Royal Society, and civilianisation almost came about, because 95 per cent of MRE's research was by then 'open'. But then came the nuclear stalemate: biological warfare became of renewed interest to the military, and MRE was not civilianised for another 20 or so years.'

The remuneration survey undertaken by the Institute in 1968 showed that remuneration levels for those in schools and technical colleges and those in industry, universities and Government service were not strikingly different until age group 36 – 40 years, after which those in industry, Government and universities tended to increase more substantially. Median salaries for Fellows and Associates of the Royal Institute of Chemistry and of Fellows and Members of the Institute were very similar up to age 35, after which chemists tended to overtake until age 55, when the position was reversed.

The Branches develop

So far we have mainly considered the work of the Institute from a perspective of its London headquarters, but an important characteristic was the steady development of regional Branches for all areas of the UK. As Mike Buttolph has described, the

Scottish Branch had been formed in 1952, followed in 1953 by London and Midland Branches. By the close of the 1960s, all regions of the UK were served by Branches. The Midlands Branch split into East and West, members feeling that the Branch was too wide — it stretched from Shrewsbury to Skegness! There was also a Branch in Eire which in 1965 became an independent Institute of Biology of Ireland. Branch activities have included symposia on diverse topics. The decade's very first issue of the *Journal* (January 1960) was devoted to a report of a Scottish Branch symposium on *Land utilisation and conservation in the Scottish Highlands*. This symposium had been organised to examine the causes of a perceived decrease in biodiversity and environmental degradation of that region.

Branch activities have also included discussions on teaching problems, visits to firms and research institutes, social events and field trips. Copp (1971) pointed out how Branch committees and, particularly, Branch Secretaries have done much to make the Institute an effective organisation throughout the country. But, as Harry Grenville has observed, it was sometimes difficult to achieve a balanced representation on Branch committees. Writing to H E Street of Leicester University in 1968, he expressed concern at the dearth of university representatives on the Midlands Branch committee, which consisted entirely of teachers and college of education lecturers. This was a reversal of the situation some 10 or 12 years earlier.

Looking through the *Journal* — which was renamed *Biologist* in 1969 — there is a strong impression that the Branches were going from strength to strength during the 1960s. Of the Scottish Branch, Bill Fletcher recalls: 'Before I became Chairman of the Scottish Branch in the early 1960s, committee meetings were invariably held at the home base of the Chairman or Secretary of the time. I determined to change this so that committee meetings were held in different locations throughout Scotland. This was enormously beneficial. Not only did it become a real 'Scottish' committee but also members of the committee visited many centres of biological teaching and research, learned of the work that was going on in them, and had the opportunity to meet the staff and hear their views.' He adds: 'Another change that I instituted was that my successor should be a woman (long overdue) and Janette Anderson (later Vice-Principal, Napier University) was appointed. When will the national body take up this option and appoint a lady to the presidency?'

We can perhaps most fittingly view the 1960s as the decade in which the Institute invested more effort and achieved more in its influence on biological education than during any other period of its 50-year history. This, together with its concern for the public's perception of biology, reflected in part underlying developments in biology itself. The 1960s marked the start of a period of rapid growth and extension of the boundaries of biological knowledge. Developments in cell biology and microbiology presaged the remarkable growth of molecular biology that we have witnessed in the last few decades. Furthermore, during the 1960s there was an evident demand for personnel in various branches of biology, particularly in agronomy and food production, and in the pharmaceutical and biochemical industries. This helped to confirm the Institute's confidence in representing a discipline which made a vital contribution to society, at least the equal to other major sciences.

References

Bottle R T and Wyatt H V (1965) The use of biological literature. *Journal of the Institute of Biology*, **12,** 59 – 60.

Brian P W (1968) Why is science unpopular? *Journal of the Institute of Biology*, **15,** 85 – 87.

Copp D J B (1971) The Institute of Biology, 1950 – 1971. *Biologist*, **18,** 2 – 9.

Despopoulos A (1964) How to get the most out of scientific literature. *Journal of the Institute of Biology*, **11,** 60 – 63.

Gardiner W (1890) *A Course of Practical Botany*. Cambridge: Cambridge University Press.

Hutchinson S A (1965) The public's ideas of biology. *Journal of the Institute of Biology*, **12,** 70 – 71.

Price Jones D (1967) Stop-press biology: let the world know. *Journal of the Institute of Biology*, **14,** 95 – 96.

Terry R J (1968) The MIBiol examination. *Journal of the Institute of Biology*, **15,** 116 – 117.

Williams P C (1965a) Suggestions for speakers and standards for slides. *Journal of the Institute of Biology*, **12,** 65 – 70.

Williams P C (1965b) The Littlewood report or the Civil Servants' Charter. *Journal of the Institute of Biology*, **12,** 141 – 145.

THE WORK OF A VICE-PRESIDENT

Diana Anderson Dip Ed PhD FRCPath CBiol FIBiol
Senior Associate and Co-ordinator of External Affairs,
BIBRA International

❝ I served both as a Vice-President of the Institute of Biology and a Chairman of its Biomedical Sciences Division. Occupying both posts simultaneously enabled me to initiate the setting up of a postgraduate Diploma in Toxicology. Phillip O'Donoghue, General Secretary of the Institute 1982–88, smoothed the path all the way through Council to ensure its final acceptance.

Dr Diana Anderson, Vice-President 1987–89.

In 1987, members of the education committee of the British Toxicology Society (BTS) asked the Institute for help developing a Diploma. As a member of the BTS scientific subcommittee at the time, this was a venture of some significance to me. Three organisations were being considered by the BTS for the Diploma: the Royal College of Pathologists, the Royal Society of Chemistry, and the Institute of Biology. The Institute was chosen because we would provide a syllabus and the Royal College of Pathologists would not; moreover, biology was considered more relevant to toxicology than chemistry. A committee was set up with representatives from both the other organisations. There were 14 members coming from all the major academic teaching organisations, industrial laboratories, and Government departments concerned with toxicology and health. The BTS education committee provided us with a working syllabus, which the members modified for the Institute to adopt. Within the year, candidates were able to sit the examination for the Diploma of the Institute of Biology in Toxicology (DIBT).

To take the examination candidates must have an honours degree, or degree equivalent, and five years' experience in an accredited laboratory. The examination consists of three parts:

- The practical tasks, which have to be carried out by participation or observation, as recorded in a logbook and countersigned by a senior toxicologist in the accredited laboratory in which the work is carried out. This obviates the need for a practical examination.
- The written examination, which consists of three papers, completed during one day at the Institute.
- After a successful examination, the candidate has to present a thesis/dissertation within the year. This can either be in the form of results of bench work and a critical review of the literature in that area, or a critical literature review of a particular topic alone. This allows candidates working in academia and industry, as well as Government positions, to obtain the Diploma. In Government posts, people tend not to have easy access to laboratory facilities.

Overseas candidates can take the examination, and some have done this. Some candidates may not wish to do the dissertation if they have already spent some years in a laboratory, they can submit six peer-reviewed published papers instead with a brief introduction and conclusion. A thesis/dissertation does not need to be presented in English, provided the summary is in English.

The examination is now in its 13th year. In 1998, it was agreed by the Institute that it could be called the International Diploma in Toxicology (IDT). It is well accepted and recognised by toxicologists in the field as an accredited qualification of the Institute of Biology. People who obtained the DIBT have the option to change their letters to IDT. Having an IDT is the easiest route to becoming registered as a toxicologist. If a person is registered in the UK, he or she is internationally accepted on the European Register of Toxicology.

Naturally, it is not a money-spinner for the Institute, because of the relatively small numbers who take the examination. The British Toxicology Society wished the qualification to be totally independent of the Society and run by the Institute since it has a Royal Charter, and so the qualifications will be acceptable throughout the European Union and elsewhere. Industry has provided fees for its running costs at the Institute for five years starting in 1998.

We view this as a success story in terms of academic and professional status for the candidates and the Institute. **99**

SOME BIOLOGY IN THE 1970s

Harry Grenville CBiol FIBiol
Former Head of Biology at Repton School, and Institute of
Biology Council 1982–84, Vice-President 1986–88

The dawn of the 1970s saw the Institute's careers advisory functions and the periodic salary surveys well established. An impressive range of symposia on biological education had been held and the *Journal of Biological Education* was three years old (although the start of John Barker's distinguished 24-year editorship was still four years away). The Institute's active interest in the teaching of applied biology in the technical colleges had spawned MIBiol by examination, which had quickly become a healthy young organism. Fifteen Branches were already up and running and we had almost 700 overseas members, amounting to just under 10 per cent of the total. A founder member, Victor Harris, put the Institute considerably into his debt by maintaining contact with many of these far-flung members in his extensive travels for the then Colonial Office in connection with his work on termites. The relations between the Institute and the other scientific institutes, such as the Biological Council, the parliamentary and scientific committee (of which Dax Copp was to become Joint Secretary) and the newly formed Council of Scientific and Technical Institutes were in a state of activity. We were offering increased services to the membership, such as discounts on insurance.

A summary of the state of play was published by Copp in the February 1971 edition of *Biologist* (Copp, 1971). It was clear that Institute membership conferred a certain status on the professional lives of the members, but possibly the most valuable service to members was the publication of the early duplicated *Bulletin*, the *Journal*, and then the sky-blue 32-page volumes of *Biologist*. The Institute became the parent of the Council for Nature and hence was involved to the full in the Countryside in 1970 Week, the British contribution to European Conservation Year. By 1970 the Institute had already distinguished itself by the high quality of its submissions to a succession of Governments. By February 1980, when Copp produced another summary reviewing the first 30 years of the Institute's activities, such briefings had become a regular part of the Institute's output.

Throughout the 1970s symposia continued to be a highly respected activity of the Institute and the topics were always chosen for their controversial nature. For instance, in the 1974 symposium on *Racial variation in man* one of the speakers was A R Jensen, who attracted considerable public opprobrium for his views on racial superiority. The press took a close interest in the proceedings, but the noisy demonstrations were confined to outside the venue. The Institute's most prestigious venture into the printed word was undoubtedly the sponsoring of the *Studies in Biology* series, which produced about 160 titles between 1966 and 1983. They were published by Edward Arnold and were widely recognised as almost compulsory reading matter for anyone who had pretensions of being well educated in biology. Their citation indices were always remarkably high. The Institute provided an impressive list of authors from among the Members and Fellows, several of them Presidents.

Growth of molecular biology

If there was one area of biology that was commanding the greatest attention during the 1970s it must have been the new science of molecular biology, particularly centring on the elucidation of the genetic code, the phenotypic expression of genes, and thus the foundation of genetic manipulation which so much exercises the public mind some 30 years after the first concepts were developed. Although the triplet code had been fully worked out before the dawn of the 1970s, progress within the discipline accelerated throughout the decade. The synthesis and characterisation of the various forms of RNA, the origin of mRNA from the DNA of bacteria (and later from the membrane-bounded nuclei of eukaryotes), and initiation and termination mechanisms of transcription and translation had all emerged during the 1960s and made phenomenal progress during the 1970s. For example, Day (1982) drew on work done in the late 1970s to foresee the use of plasmids in inserting genes into eukaryotic cells, so important in medical, veterinary and agronomic practice. Jackson (1978) set out details of the export of proteins from ribosomes bound to the endoplasmic reticulum of eukaryotic cells and recognised the central importance of this mechanism in genetic manipulation in what was then the future. The bearing that the techniques of molecular biology developed during the 1970s would have on genetic manipulation was well summarised by Ray Gibson in his article in *Biologist* (Gibson, 1982). A brief overview of recombinant DNA techniques, such as the handling of plasmids and the reverse transcription of eukaryotic genes, was followed by a survey of their potential applications in medicine, industry and agriculture. The ease and low-cost production of human enzymes, interferon, diagnostic and therapeutic enzymes, and rapid progress towards clinical trials was foreseen. Gibson forecast the use of manipulated microorganisms in the energy industry. Fuel alcohol in the form of a product of cellulose digestion would be widely used. This technology has certainly got off the ground, but while the economic stranglehold of the oil and natural gas industries remains tight a full take-off seems unlikely. The development of a pseudomonad which can degrade oil has certainly been achieved on an industrial scale, but each major oil spill seems to overwhelm the best efforts of the organisms. Like many other prophetic writers of the period, including that enthusiast for nitrogen fixation John Postgate, Gibson thought that the holy grail of agricultural innovation, the splicing of the nitrogen-fixing ability of microorganisms into non-leguminous cereal crops, would be attained shortly. At the turn of the century the practical difficulties of translating theory into agricultural practice remain formidable. A careful examination of the biotechnological prognoses of the 1970s reveals a paradoxical gap. No one at the time foresaw that crops could be generated and tested on a farm scale that would have the ability to withstand weed-killers and incorporate their own insecticides. This is clearly far less invasive than wholesale spraying with chemical pesticides, yet less than 30 years later newspaper headlines were warning of apocalypse and activists were trashing experimental crops.

Changing values

Attitudes in 1970 were very different from those of the present day. As an example, what are we to make of the following exchange reported during the discussion after a March 1970 symposium on *The future pattern of the training and employment of biologists*:

> Professor P N Campbell (Leeds University): 'Women need to have better grades at A-level than do men to study medicine at Leeds University.'

> A headmistress: 'Unfortunately such discrimination is widespread among medical schools, but is it justifiable?'

> Professor G Belyavin (University College Hospital): 'The reason is partly historical; accommodation was designed for men and consequently there are more places available for the male sex. Further, training a doctor is very costly and men are a better investment than women since they continue their work after marrying!'

Even if we assume that this had an element of tongue in cheek, such remarks would be unthinkable in the new millennium, even in fun.

An era of expansion

In 1971 Copp foresaw what was soon to become a major preoccupation for the Institute. One can almost feel the anxiety in the bald statement that a staff of 20 were trying to work in the rabbit warren of tiny maids' rooms four floors up at 41 Queen's Gate. Although we remained grateful to the Royal Entomological Society for the relatively low rent they charged us, the urgency of finding premises of our own was becoming acute. There seems never to have been a time when the Institute was not strapped for cash. The recessions following the 1973 oil crisis and again in the early 1980s bore down on the Institute as on everyone else. Nevertheless, by 1979 a building fund was set up, starting with £20 000. As we shall see in the following chapter, just three years later it became possible to buy 20 Queensberry Place.

Membership increased steadily during the decade, growing from 6346 in 1969 to 13 335 in 1979. This fuelled an increase in our subscription income from about £24 000 to about £120 000. Although the number of members increased by 110 per cent, the total value of their subscriptions went up by 500 per cent. Although the phrase 'you can't buck the market' began to gain currency in the late 1970s, the Institute seems to have managed it up to a point. This was not achieved without some pain. Inflation was rampant in the mid-1970s and subscriptions were raised twice in successive years. John Abbott, the Honorary Treasurer, registered 'dismay' at having to recommend an increase of 25 per cent in 1976 (members' subscriptions were increased from £10.00 to £12.50). The previous year's increase had been even worse — 75 per cent. But the Treasurer was able to sugar the pill slightly by pointing out that offsetting the subscription against the 35 per cent rate of income tax helped to cushion the blow. By contrast, Abbott reported that he was 'pleased to be able to give members encouraging news' in time for their 1978/79 subscriptions: they would remain unchanged. In some measure this was due to a majority of members paying by direct debit, representing a great saving in postage costs. Another factor was increased recruiting. A J Abbott (1930–91) spent all his working life at Long Ashton Research Station of Bristol University, researching plant tissue culture and micropropagation. His distinguished period as Honorary Treasurer of the Institute (1975–79) was marked by a transformation from a distinctly weak position to one of stability. He was an enthusiast for the Royal Charter, believing that financial strength would ultimately be gained from the new status. During his time as Treasurer the negotiations for the acquisition of 20 Queensberry Place were successfully concluded, involving a very large bank loan negotiated by Abbott and A C Mohan.

Questionnaires were sent out to Members and Fellows at approximately two-year intervals to establish their level of remuneration. In 1977 almost 25 per cent of the membership responded. The results were presented in six tables giving income levels according to age, class of membership, comparisons with 1974 and 1971, field of employment and level of qualification. Finally, a table surveyed pensions according to the year in which members retired. We can record some of those conclusions. The median level of income for all grades of members aged 41 – 45 was £6700; for Fellows alone in the same age group it was £9275. The rates of increase for Fellows were 52 per cent during 1974–77 and 26 per cent in 1971–74. For Members the equivalent increases were 85 per cent and 16 per cent. It is clear that Members managed to keep abreast of inflation rather better than Fellows. Almost exactly half the membership were employed in education, of whom a third were in schools and almost another third in universities. Industry occupied 16 per cent, the majority in pharmaceuticals. Twenty-seven per cent were in the public sector, of whom there were very nearly twice as many in research institutes than in central and local government, hospitals and the water industry combined.

The Institute put a considerable effort into monitoring the first employment of biologists after they qualified. As early as May 1970 an entire issue of *Biologist* was devoted to careers with contributions by leaders in their fields on management, bio-chemistry, ecology, education, and HNC in Applied Biology, together with a list of all the colleges offering the courses. In November of the same year an attempt was made to forecast future employment in Government, medical research, human science, in polytechnics and the possible non-vocational uses of biology degrees. In 1975 our survey revealed that 173 out of 4698 were unemployed but only 799 out of the 1464 who entered full-time employment were employed in posts that were related to their training. If this shows anything it is that graduate biologists are remarkably adaptable, a phenomenon first noticed in World War II when a substantial number of those engaged in operational research had actually been trained as biologists.

In the 1970s the Institute had a highly enthusiastic Education Officer, Barry Gregson-Allcott. In January 1976 he contributed an article to the *Daily Telegraph* in which he outlined a remarkable range of destinations for qualified biologists. Later in the same year Gregson-Allcott produced an eight-page guide to careers and courses in biology. This listed about 50 career guide publications with prices and the addresses of the suppliers. Apart from general information on degree courses there were sections on agriculture, biochemistry, pharmacology, and so on, as well as a range of publica-tions issued by Government departments and other public bodies. There was even a section of information on student grants. Anyone in possession of this duplicated, typewritten document would hardly need to look anywhere else for information.

Coming of age

The Institute marked its 21st anniversary with a celebration meeting held 31 March – 2 April 1971 at Imperial College, London. The London Branch laid on a conver-sazione visited by 600 individuals and the total attendance, including a symposium on the *Future of man* and a splendid dinner, totalled over 1000. The presence of Edward Hindle, Jim Danielli, and Bob Harris, the founding President, Honorary Secretary, and Honorary Treasurer respectively, lent an air of special significance to the occasion.

But in January 1973 Hindle died at the age of 87. It truly was the end of an era. The Professor of Tropical Medicine at Liverpool when the young Hindle joined as a junior member of staff had been Sir Ronald Ross (1857–1932), winner of the 1902 Nobel Prize in Medicine for his pioneering work on malaria. In March the Institute's President, Kenneth Mellanby, addressed a Memorial Service in St James's, Piccadilly. As he reminded the congregation, Hindle was almost certainly the last of the founder members of the Institute to have graduated (in 1906) from the old Royal College of Science, the forerunner of today's Imperial College. Early in his scientif-ic career his main interest focused on parasites, but he was no narrow specialist, pay-

Dr Edward Hindle, first President of the Institute 1950–52. This bust, by Peter Lambda, is on display in the Institute's Committee room.

ing attention also to crustacea, echinoderms and marine plankton. He then spent two years at La Jolla Marine Station in California. One wonders if a 1999 worker at that renowned institute could begin to visualise Hindle's life there in 1909, when California was scarcely out of the frontier tradition. Hindle spent the war years in the Royal Engineers and in 1919 became Professor of Biology in the Medical School in Cairo. By 1924 he was back in England at the London School of Hygiene and Tropical Medicine and threw himself into a veritable torrent of research in China, West Africa, back at the Wellcome Research Laboratories and the London School of Hygiene and Tropical Medicine, and, finally, as Regius Professor of Zoology at Glasgow University. Among Hindle's many other achievements, undoubtedly his greatest contribution was the development of a vaccine against yellow fever. In many ways the Institute owes its existence to Hindle, and it was inevitable that he would become our founder President. If anyone is in any doubt as to the vigour and integrity of the man they should look long and hard at Peter Lambda's bronze portrait bust at Queensberry Place. This is the original: the National Portrait Gallery thought it was important enough as a work of art to make a replica and return the original to the Institute.

The Divisions expand

Shortly after Hindle's death the Agricultural Sciences Division was inaugurated, to be followed in 1975 by the Biomedical Division. The Environmental and Education Divisions followed later in 1976 (the earlier biological education committee was a joint body with the Royal Society). The vigorous London Biology Teachers' Group began life in 1971, while in 1975 the European Community Biologists' Association (ECBA) saw the light of day. Arguably Copp was its chief midwife and the then Honorary Secretary Philip O'Donoghue chaired the first two meetings. Its invaluable spadework ensured the mutual recognition of biological qualifications between member states which culminated eventually in the designation of EurBiol.

All four of the Institute's Divisions managed to attract extremely eminent scientists to address their inaugural meetings on subjects of importance. The inaugural meetings were very well attended, with audiences between 150 to over 300 biologists. First off the mark was the Agricultural Sciences Division, on 29 June 1973. This was double-headed by W H Henderson, Secretary of the Agricultural Research Council, and H C Pereira, the new Chief Scientist under the arrangements spelled out in the Rothschild report. Their subject was *The future of agricultural research and development.*

A year later came the Biomedical Division's inaugural meeting on 25 June 1974, which was addressed by Sir Frederick Dainton on the subject of *Scientific research and the State*. Environment and Education followed each other closely in 1976, on 5 November and 17 December respectively. Martin Holdgate spoke to the former on *Biologists in environmental management* and Mellanby addressed the new Education Division on *Truth and enthusiasm in biological education*.

In his memorable 1974 address, Sir Frederick put it to the Biomedical Division that the relationship between the state and scientific endeavour began with committees in World War I that regularised scientists' work in the war effort. The Research Councils sprang from these committees, and Government was obliged, rather reluctantly, to conclude that it had to support scientific research. He saw four characteristics of scientific pursuits: first, technology in support of a specific goal (e.g. space travel); secondly, 'blue-sky' research with no particular end-product in view, but which has almost invariably turned out to have important application (e.g. Einstein's ideas and nuclear energy applications); third, the interaction between technology and science itself (e.g. high-energy particle accelerators); and, finally, the effect of scientific hypotheses on the cultural and philosophical foundations of society (e.g. Darwinism). These axioms notwithstanding, Sir Frederick saw a change of mood in the early 1970s when society tended to turn away from science — 'the beginning of the end of euphoria'. He considered that scientists may not have done enough to communicate with the public. Since Government represents the public, the Treasury paymasters were becoming less forthcoming in support of science. Throughout his career Sir Frederick had strongly urged that a flow of high-quality science graduates must be maintained and that some of the flow should be directed towards Government. He characterised the rationale behind the Rothschild report as a directed funnelling of resources from the public purse towards strategic research carried out by socially and economically aware scientists in partnership with responsible Government departments. Of course, in those early days of Rothschild it was still possible to take a sanguine view of its operation, but the defects showed up later.

Some key figures

Kenneth Mellanby CBE (1908–93) was the Institute's President in 1972–73. Even if his presidency had not been marked by any other achievements (and there were plenty) he would have been remembered as the prime mover in the establishment of the Divisions. Although he was arguably best known to the general public for his volume in the *New Naturalist* series, *Pesticides and Pollution,* a pioneering book in the tradition of Rachel Carson's *Silent Spring,* he had also been an academic administrator in Nigeria where he established and directed the University College of Ibadan. People who knew him well itched at the very thought of the research he conducted on scabies during the war, experimenting on himself and volunteer conscientious objectors. During 1955–61 he was head of entomology at Rothamsted and in 1961–74 Director of the Monks Wood Experimental Station. Mellanby came from the right sort of stable: his mother, Helen, was a noted naturalist and the author of a much-loved book on freshwater biology, and her son an unusually outgoing and energetic crusader in the cause of environmental conservation.

Another significant link with the earliest days of the Institute was broken in 1975 with the death of H J 'Bill' Bunker, born in 1897. A number of senior founder members had seen active service in World War I just as now, at the turn of the millennium, we have a minority of elderly biologists who were active in World War II. When requests were made for reminiscences for this volume, it was noticeable how many contributions from prominent members and Fellows mentioned Bill as a formative influence in the earlier parts of their careers. His own sphere of industrial microbiology started unexpectedly enough in 1922 at the RN Cordite Factory on the shores of Poole Harbour. The Navy, with unusual insight, realised that a biologist would be a good investment when considering the disposal of cellulose waste from explosives manufacture. Bunker went on to pioneer research on sulphate-reducing bacteria and finally he was in charge of the purpose-built research department of Barclay Perkin's brewery. In 1956 two breweries merged and Bunker set up as an independent consultant. After this enforced change in direction there was no holding him. He advised almost 100 industrial undertakings on microbiological problems until he finally died in harness. In a 53-year working life he seems to have made vast circles of friends and no enemies. Bunker was a Council member at our beginning; he served twice as Vice-President, then as Honorary Secretary and finally as President (1967–69). As far as can be ascertained he and his wife, Marie, began the presidential tradition of visiting all the Branches. As we have seen, at the time of Hindle's death some of the major Divisions sprang into life, so the first stirrings of the quest for the Royal Charter followed Bunker's demise.

Another of the Institute's Presidents from the early years (1962–63) died in the 1970s. He was Sir Gerard Thornton (1892–1977). His work, mainly at Rothamsted, concerned legume root symbiosis with soil microorganisms and laid the foundations for the later, clearer understanding of nitrogen fixation. The biological education committee was set up jointly with the Royal Society at Thornton's instigation. Two aspects of the Institute's work which we now take for granted began during his presidency: the Darwin Lectures and the institution of Fellowships. The whole world was astonished when, in 1978, Louise Brown was born after *in vitro* fertilisation, but Institute members had already heard of the details of this work in R G Edwards'

Darwin Lecture in 1971 on human conception. All the aims of work in the field were comprehensively surveyed. Need anyone ask whether the Institute was doing its job of keeping members informed of current trends?

The Institute suffered a particularly sad blow when the immediate Past-President, Sir Frederick Bawden, died in March 1972, only two months after the end of his presidential term. He had trained as a virologist and spent almost all his professional life at Rothamsted, becoming Director in 1958. He was a successful administrator while continuing active research and maintaining close links with the farming community. In his obituary, Mellanby spoke of Bawden as a direct negation of the Rothschild thesis that directors of scientific institutions should be pure administrators. The diminishing number who were members of the Institute in Bawden's time remember his deep concern with the conservation of the environment. The obituary appeared in the May 1972 *Biologist*, which was a special issue on the environment with distinguished contributions from T R E Southwood and Martin Holdgate. Southwood concentrated minds wonderfully at the time by summarising the various outlooks for the future of humanity, ranging from the pessimism of Paul Ehrlich to the supreme optimism of John Maddox in his editorials in *Nature*.

A mid-decade review

In the issue of *Biologist* for August 1975 O'Donoghue published a summary of the Institute's activities. This annotated list came midway between two annual reports of the Honorary Secretary and it provides an valuable insight into our endeavours halfway through our existence.

- The European Community Biologists' Association (ECBA) had just started work on mutual recognition of qualifications.
- The Cruelty to Animals Act 1876 was coming up to its centenary revision and the Institute was actively preparing to represent its views to the Government on animal research, production and testing.
- R J C Harris chaired a committee preparing the Institute's advice to the Advisory Board for the Research Councils.
- The Schools Council had asked the Institute to produce the biology syllabuses for the new N and F examinations. This was done a little later by the new Education Division, and it is a sad reflection on the political process that the effort turned out to be a work of supererogation.
- C H Collins of Dulwich Hospital Public Health Laboratory produced a leaflet, with a bibliography, on safety in educational establishments.
- The Biological Information Service was inaugurated in April 1975; it was jointly sponsored by the Institute and the British Library. This pioneering database could be retrieved by computer from *Biosis Previews* (akin to *Biological Abstracts)*,

original research reports and reviews, and documentation on the history and philosophy of biology and on biomedical topics.
- The employment of biologists by the newly established regional water authorities was under consideration.
- The Biomedical and Agriculture Divisions interested themselves in specialist education and career structure and the future of the appropriate Research Councils. Discussions to launch the Education and Environment Divisions were well under way and their inaugural meetings took place in the following year.

During the mid-1970s the Institute was at the heart of a great many activities. We were involved in a dozen joint organisations or confederations. Mention has already been made of the ECBA and the Biological Information Service, but others included:

- The Biological Council, by this time embracing 109 specialist societies.
- The Council of Science and Technology Institutes (CSTI), which represented 60 000 qualified scientists and was a powerful voice in employment and remuneration matters.
- The joint affairs committee of CSTI and the Council of Engineering Institutions.
- The joint affairs committee which initiated the Council for Environmental Science and Engineering, tried to influence the Government on environmental matters.
- The Professional Institutions Council for Conservation (PICC), which arose from the *Countryside in 1970* conference and brought together many bodies concerned with conservation, including architecture, planning and forestry.
- The biological education committee, jointly with the Royal Society, later to be subsumed into the Education Division.
- Joint committees with the Department of Education and Science and the Scottish Education Department to supervise courses for ONC, HNC and HND in Applied Biology.
- The Parliamentary and scientific committee, an unofficial group of members of both Houses of Parliament and representatives of scientific bodies.

Honorary Secretaries who later became Presidents are rare enough, but they outnumber by two to one Honorary Secretaries who became General Secretaries. This is O'Donoghue's unique translation, which would be achieved when Copp retired in 1982. His years as Honorary Secretary (1972–76) included such key developments as the establishment of the Divisions, the early negotiations for the Charter and the birth of ECBA. He had been employed at the ARC Field Station at Compton, the Dairying Research Institute and the Royal Postgraduate Medical School as lecturer with responsibility for the animal houses and the editorship of the journal *Laboratory Animals*. His Honorary Secretary's reports to the Institute's AGMs were always eagerly anticipated for their polished style and wit, as were the events for which O'Donoghue oversaw the arrangements for food and drink.

Scientific freedom

The distinguished editor of *Biologist*, L R Taylor, decided in February 1973 to print a declaration with the title 'Scientific freedom', published by 50 eminent scientists. Though most were American the list included Francis Crick, Jacques Monod, Hans Eysenk, Conrad Darlington and John (later Sir John) Kendrew. The group demanded that investigations into hereditary factors contributing to human behaviour and abilities should proceed without censure, suppression or punishment for reasons of ideology. The signatories believed themselves to be liable to condemnation as heretics or even fascists by practitioners in fields such as sociology, social anthropology, educational psychology, etc. Comments from members were invited and seven of them were duly published in the following May. Not unexpectedly there was support for and opposition to the signatories. While deploring personal attacks on the proponents of 'hereditarianism', some of the correspondents revealed themselves as somewhat illiberal opponents. One, in effect, said 'how dare they put their work on an equal footing with Galileo, Darwin or Einstein?'

Chartered biologists

Throughout the decade, first the officers, then Council and eventually the membership wrestled with the decision to seek chartered status for our Institute. As early as May 1975 members were asked in *Biologist* to consider the advantages and to make their views known. A working party chaired by Mellanby had slaved away for months, in liaison with the Institutes of Chemistry, Physics and Metallurgy, to discover what was involved. By November 1975 the President, J Heslop-Harrison, announced that Council had recommended that an application should be made as it would fortify the position of biologists in relation to UK and EEC legislation if they had chartered status. The subsequent AGM in January 1976 revealed that the referendum of the membership had produced a majority of 937 to 18 in favour of petitioning for a Royal Charter. There followed three years of intense beavering away at drafting the petition. General Secretary Copp, President G E Fogg, later R J C Harris, and Vice-President P N Wilson, Chairman of the Working Party on the Charter, certainly had their hands full during this time.

The proposal involved contacts with such non-biological bodies as the Privy Council, represented by its extremely helpful Clerk Neville E Leigh CVO, the College of Arms, and the constitutional law firm of Allen and Overy. At one point

The Royal Charter of the Institute of Biology granted by Her Majesty in 1979.

the Inland Revenue questioned whether charitable status could be maintained, but Allen and Overy saw them off by drafting in a merger between the Trust Fund for publishing purposes and the company limited by guarantee for all other activities. The Charter was received in March 1979, along with the right to bear a coat of arms, but to the regret of some members it had been realised that the prefix 'Royal' was to be applied for at a future date. What seemed to matter more was the designation CBiol than the letters MRIBiol. The entire exercise was crowned by a Charter reception in January 1980, hosted by the new President, E J W Barrington, at the Natural History Museum. It was attended by 350 members and a clutch of distinguished guests, including David (now Sir David) Attenborough and Sir Michael Swann.

Apart from Mellanby, three 1970s Presidents were particularly preoccupied with paving the road to the Charter: Heslop-Harrison, Fogg and Harris. J Heslop-Harrison FRS was the immediate successor of Mellanby and will be remembered for his enthusiastic advocacy of chartered status for the Institute. The matter had first been mooted in the May 1975 *Biologist* by Copp and strongly endorsed a few months later by Heslop-Harrison, who then persuaded Council to recommend to the membership that the grant of a Charter should be applied for. Heslop-Harrison's first chair was at Queen's University, Belfast, and later at Birmingham and Wisconsin. He was an early enthusiast for integration of university courses in botany and zoology and he was the first Chairman of the combined School of Biological Sciences at Birmingham. At the time of his presidency Heslop-Harrison was Director of the Royal Botanic Gardens, Kew, possibly a matter of coming events casting their shadow before them. Another Director of Kew is Sir Ghillean Prance, our first President in the 21st century. Heslop-Harrison's presidential address of 1975 on *Crops, commodities and energy capture* was prophetic in its insistence that renewable sources of energy have to be seriously investigated to secure the future of *Homo sapiens* on the earth in the long run.

G E Fogg CBE FRS marked his presidency with an enormous amount of work, not only by himself but by Vice-President Peter Wilson and General Secretary Copp as they smoothed the way towards the Royal Charter. Fogg and R J C Harris were the only two Honorary Secretaries of the Institute who later became Presidents. Fogg's wartime work for the Ministry of Supply on seaweed resources led to his employment by Pest Control Ltd, arguably the first commercial undertaking to concern itself with selective herbicides. He held chairs of botany at Westfield College and marine biology at Bangor. There were two opportunities for him to make research visits to Antarctica, and he was elected to be Chairman of the Freshwater Biological Association, among other extra-curricular activities.

R J C Harris (1922–80) was not only the first Honorary Secretary and Honorary Treasurer of the Institute but later (1978–79) served as the President who, with Copp, actually received the Royal Charter from the Queen. He became involved in preparing the celebrations over which his successor, E J W Barrington, presided. After a long career in cancer research, mainly at the Chester Beatty Institute, Harris became Director of the Microbiological Research Establishment at Porton Down in 1971 until his retirement eight years later. It was particularly tragic that he died only a few months after the end of his presidency.

Education and change

Educationalists inside and outside the Institute were plagued during the second half of the 1970s by a Ministry of Education proposal that GCE A-levels should be replaced by N(ormal) and F(urther) level examinations, while leaving S levels untouched. Five subjects were to be studied, including one or two at F level. The worthy aim was to broaden the basis of post-16 education, as a preparation for both tertiary education and the world of work. The Schools Council took pains to ensure the widest possible discussion among school and university teachers, employers and the general public. Hundreds of meetings in all conceivable forums were held all over the country. Our own Education Division set out the arguments as they affected biology in the September 1978 *Biologist* and invited members to discuss their paper at Chelsea College in November. By early 1979 syllabuses had been drawn up, authors had even produced textbooks aimed at the new levels, and the introduction of the new system seemed imminent. As far as can be ascertained it was the solitary decision of the Minister Shirley Williams which brought the whole edifice crashing to the ground amid mutterings about the sanctity of A-levels as the British educational gold standard and the envy of lesser mortals. Never before or since can the mountain of the educational establishment have laboured so mightily for no practical benefit.

Unforeseen difficulties arose in the mid-1970s between some schoolteacher members and most of the medical schools. Most of the teachers who taught biology in their sixth forms had prospective medical students among their pupils. In some independent schools such aspiring young medical students were actually in the majority. The medical educators had convinced themselves that too many of their incoming students were insufficiently numerate to cope with the demands of the physical and chemical aspects of the preclinical syllabus. A frequent comment was that 'medicine is becoming ever more scientific'. (When was it ever otherwise?) The medical schools eventually began to accept, and later actually to prefer, applicants who presented themselves with three A-levels in chemistry, physics and mathematics, with biology at O-level. In one exchange between an independent school head of biology and a Midland medical school it emerged that human biology at the slightly more elevated AO-level would not be accepted. The letter of rebuttal stipulated: 'We said O-level biology and we will stick to it.' The traditional A-level combination of biology, chemistry and physics with maths at AO-level was similarly blacklisted. The newly hatched Education Division did its best to support the teachers, but had not yet acquired sufficient authority to take on the combined might of the medical schools. It was a wise move on their part to hold a symposium in 1977 at which speakers from both sides were followed by a detailed discussion. A very small-scale research project among first-year Cambridge medical students in 1978 revealed that about half of them had arrived without A-level biology. They felt disadvantaged because they had lost two years' worth of microscopy, and their concept of the human animal was sketchy by their not having been formally taught evolution, but they were confident that they would catch up in the course of their first year. The entire controversy evaporated in the subsequent years when it became ever more common for A-level candidates to present with four or even five A-levels.

Rationalising the Fellowship

Several Presidents were keen to increase the proportion of Fellows among the membership and as a result the Fellowship committee had by the 1970s developed a *modus operandi* of considerable complexity. An existing Fellow (the proposer) would write to three other members, of whom two also had to be Fellows (the candidate's supporters). The proposers approached members whom they knew well who were willing to be put forward for Fellowship and who would nominate some or all of the supporters. The criteria were to include extent and length of service to biology, more particularly focusing on special distinction in their field of endeavour, be it research, teaching or administration. A proposal was then put to the Fellowship committee for discussion at their next meeting. The result of their deliberations was communicated to the proposer and the candidate.

There was nothing intrinsically wrong with the procedure and in the great majority of cases proposals were accepted to the satisfaction of all concerned, to the extent that almost 250 Fellows were elected between 1972 and 1976, and by 1975 there were in addition 15 Honorary Fellows who had been directly nominated by Council. The committee, of course, did not have to experience the subsequent relationship between a proposer and an unsuccessful candidate. At best an air of embarrassment was experienced by both parties and at worst applicants may have felt that they had been made to pass through a complicated procedure imposed by a distant committee. What made matters worse was the 'rejection slip', which was brusque in tone. It read, in full:

'Dear … The Fellowship committee of the Institute recently discussed your Fellowship nomination. Regrettably I must inform you that they felt unable to rec ommend your election. Yours sincerely, … General Secretary.'

To compound the slight that some experienced, rejections were signed by the General Secretary while elections were communicated personally under the hand of the Honorary Secretary. The composition of Institute committees changed regularly and something of this difficulty may have communicated itself to later incumbents. The present system is far better in this respect: members who believe that they may be qualified now make their own applications, and biologists whose achievements approach those worthy of a DSc are encouraged to apply.

Branches from strength to strength

A glance through *Biologist* in the 1970s reveals the tremendous range of Branch activities, with lectures, symposia, visits including field trips, and joint activities with neighbouring Branches. They were all adequately advertised under 'Forthcoming events' and appropriate fliers were distributed with the journal. In those days stuffing envelopes with the correct documents was still done in-house and must have represented a considerable drain on staff time when staffing was tighter. A brief look at one area gives a flavour of what was happening. The unwieldy Midlands Branch had already split into East and West at the outset of the 1970s, although the density of population and of academic institutions in the Derby-Nottingham-Leicester triangle made it inevitable that many joint activities were organised, sometimes to the chagrin of the numerous Birmingham members who saw no reason to travel to the eastern edge of their West Midlands stronghold. As one organiser said, 'The West Midlanders have an ineradicable impression that Derbyshire lies about 120 miles beyond a sort of St Gotthart Pass where the permanent snow-line descends to 1500 feet regularly every mid-September.'

The East Midlands Branch marked the 21st anniversary in 1971 with a symposium entitled *Human genetics*, featuring such distinguished contributors as Cyril (later Sir Cyril) Clarke FRS and C O Carter. The symposium was held in the School of Botany and Zoology of Nottingham University, after which everyone moved to the centre of the city for a celebration dinner at Trent Polytechnic. The members of the West Midlands Branch ranged widely within their own area. For example, in 1972 there were meetings on the *Biology of disease* at Birmingham, *Conservation and agriculture* near Warwick and *Environmental control* at the Ministry of Agriculture, Fisheries and Food, Wolverhampton, which was followed by the AGM at St Paul's College of Education (a former nunnery), with an address given by K Mather FRS. The East Midlands Branch arranged a pioneering meeting in 1973 on the *Institute of Biology in the future*. The Honorary Secretary, O'Donoghue, spoke on *The Institute: for biologists or for society?*, Vivian Wyatt spoke on *When the doubling stops*, and H E Street considered *The role of the Institute in technical education*. It had now become a tradition for Presidents to visit Branches as much as they could during their term of office. Thus Mellanby addressed a Branch dinner at Leicester University in 1973, the first of several such high-level contacts between the East Midlands Branch and headquarters.

A very interesting visit was paid by West Midlands in 1974 to Ufton Fields, a 77-acre former quarry site near Leamington Spa, whose recolonisation was being monitored by the Warwickshire Nature Conservation Trust. Again and again when looking at Branch or central records one notices how often they anticipated coming events. Thus in 1974 D C Burke told members of the West Midlands Branch about *Interferon: past history and future hopes*.

A break with a 25-year tradition came in 1975, when the Institute's annual general meeting was held for the first time outside London — in Birmingham. This required more administration than usual. A new departure was to find overnight hosts for members travelling longer distances after the meeting. The number of constitutional amendments was greater than for several past AGMs. In the mid-1970s many agricultural scientists were concerned with overall energy relationships between crops and the environment. Two later Presidents, Sir Kenneth Blaxter and Sir Colin Spedding, were among the pioneers in this field of research. It is not surprising that it surfaced in the presidential address of the Birmingham meeting: Heslop-Harrison spoke on *Crops, commodities and energy capture*. The new venture was successful enough to encourage the Institute to hold the next non-London AGM in that region, at Nottingham in 1978.

Some independent schools were chosen to host Branch meetings in the later 1970s, presumably on account of their catering facilities: Warwick in 1978 and Repton in 1975 and again in 1980, marking the occasion of the Charter meeting, a joint venture between both Midland Branches. It was said at the time that Repton, in the East Midlands Branch area, was so close to the western boundary that a stone vigorously thrown could be made to fall in the West Midlands. An unusual occasion

At an East and West Midlands Branch Meeting at Repton School: (l to r) Mrs Janet Dean, Dr John Gunn, Dr John Marsden, Mr E C Herwin, the late Sir Kenneth Blaxter (President of the Institute), Mr Harry Grenville.

was a symposium on *Archaeology and biology* held at Derby College of Technology (the future University of Derby) in March 1979, with speakers from both disciplines.

At this time the Institute was known for its striking symbol, based on the ancient mark of yin and yang. The foremost scholar of the history of Chinese science, Sir Joseph Needham, contributed a note to *Biologist* in 1977 concerning the meaning of the symbol. He pointed out that the dark side of the disc, yin, stands for darkness, autumn and winter, the female and the negative. The light side represents brightness, spring and summer, the male and the positive. This dualism is not to be regarded as antagonistic, but a unity contributed to by two forces, a 2400-year-old concept of Chinese philosophy. Just as one side of the disc reaches its greatest diameter so the other begins its rise to dominance. The Institute's additions of a hand in the yang and a leafy twig in the yin to represent the animal and the plant kingdoms kept close to the Chinese notions of movement and stillness.

Lighter moments

During the decade there was evidence of lighthearted moments in the Institute's affairs. The 'No comment' column in *Biologist* was always appreciated for its deft puncturing of other people's dignity, and Council meetings were frequently marked by bursts of hilarity. Sometimes longer contributions to *Biologist* lightened the atmosphere a little. For example, Jack Cohen's comments on Finagle's Laws in May 1977 included the Ninth Law: 'The only books and records which get lost are those one particularly wishes to keep.' As a corollary he added the Law of Homoiopracty:

One of the cartoons illustrating Margaret E Cooper's articles on Law for Biologists.

'They are returned by the borrower one week after replacements have been bought.' Ustilago Nuda wrote in May 1976 on The promotion of phytopathology, claiming that to promote the interests and welfare of phytopathologists an extensive programme had been initiated, with the sole aim of creating new problems. For example, when fruit research was threatened by Government cutbacks, 'colleagues in the land of prunes and slivovic' obliged by supplying the sharka virus, thereby ensuring the continued employment of plant pathologists. In November 1975 a 'Molecular Genesis' began: 'In the beginning was the Word and the Word was Hydrogen' and ended: 'Let the coacervates respond to the environment and grow. Let them multiply and colonise all the corners of the Earth. And let each coacervate be called a cell.'

Starting at the end of 1978, and running for two years, a series of six expert articles by Margaret E Cooper LLB appeared in *Biologist*. They are accompanied by witty cartoons which, although unsigned, one suspects are the work of the author. In the article on aspects of biomedical law there is a drawing of a crude homemade still labelled 'Ole Granfer Puke's "Bust ma Gizzard" Moonshine Remedy' above the caption 'Licences are required to manufacture medicinal products …'. All the articles are remarkably comprehensive and deal with such topics as Animal Experiment Law (very topical at the time just after the Cruelty to Animals Act 1876 had been amended), Animal Welfare Law (important to those in charge of animal houses in research establishments), Wildlife Conservation Law (affecting ringing procedures of wild birds, protection of rare plants, etc) and measures of official control over plants and animals used by biologists, such as regulations covering animal movement, import and export, and the Convention on International Trade in Endangered Species (CITES) regulations as they affect the United Kingdom. Before these articles appeared, no doubt most biological practitioners knew what they needed to know about the legal requirements governing their own work, but little or nothing about the ways in which their colleagues in other specialities were affected.

Spreading the word

Throughout the 1970s the Institute was increasingly regarded as a source of authoritative insight into all biological matters. In February 1972 the Institute responded to the Government's invitation to comment on the Rothschild proposals, which were published as a Command Paper in July of that year. The Green Paper became notorious for suggesting that British science should be organised on a so-called 'customer/contractor' basis, where the customers would be largely Government departments under the aegis of their new chief scientists (with possible restrictions on freedom of publication due to departmental policy) and the contractors would be the research councils and university departments. The Institute, in its detailed response, pointed to the dangers this would pose to the research councils, whose support of university research students had been so valuable. The councils' resources for sponsoring research would be severely restricted. Rothschild drew a distinction between pure and applied research: the latter was to be largely subsumed in the customer/contractor category. The 1980s were not yet two months old when a note in the 'Comment' column of *Biologist* was saying to the Government, in as many words, 'we told you so'. The pressures on 'blue-sky' research came from general cuts in expenditure as well as from a shift towards applied research grants from the ARC, the MRC and NERC. It is doubtful whether the consequences of the elucidation of the genetic code achieved during the 1970s would have been as fully exploited as they were, had the Rothschild proposals taken such a hold at the beginning of the decade as they had by its end.

Molecular biology continued to make progress, but increasingly found itself (at least in Britain) confronting a lack of support because of a curious perception that the work was insufficiently 'applied'. The Institute had, meanwhile, forged ahead during the decade in the face of financial stringencies and a variety of public controversies so that, by the end of the decade, we were clearly a force to be reckoned with in British biology.

References

Copp D J B (1971) The Institute of Biology, 1950 – 1971. *Biologist,* **18,** 2 – 9.

Day M (1982) *Plasmids.* Studies in Biology No 142.

Gibson R (1982) An insider's view from Cadbury Schweppes plc. *Biologist,* **29,** 191 – 197.

Jackson R (1978) *Protein Synthesis.* Carolina Biology Readers No. 86.

AT THE GRASS ROOTS

Marianne Overton CIBiol MIBiol
Chairman of East Midlands Branch

❝ Strange to tell, on starting work aged 22 I actually missed attending university lectures and surprised myself by thoroughly enjoying a local Institute lecture on *Sleep,* in Northampton. I was impressed by the fact that the meeting appeared to be very pleasantly and efficiently run by a woman — who was not slow in inviting me to join the committee. It was 13 years before I reached the heady heights of Chairman of the Branch, mainly because I had enjoyed being Secretary so much. I found that serving the Institute of Biology opened doors, in that people knew me and I could talk freely with all manner of otherwise intimidating, illustrious old

Mrs Marianne Overton, Secretary of the East Midlands Branch 1987–98 and Branch Chairman from 1998.

dons. The Branch has always been completely free of petty jealousies, anxieties about promotion or any other 'baggage' of the work environment, so that all the meetings have been very much about welcoming people and involving everyone in such interesting conversations that the journey always seems most worthwhile.

The biggest events the Branch has organised (with over 200 people attending) have been *Is human evolution over?* with Steve Jones (the answer is yes, he says); the *Armageddon debate,* about whether technology is bringing the end of the human race, with a brilliant line-up of speakers; *Plant biotechnology;* and the weekend on Sir Joseph Banks at Lincoln Cathedral, which resulted in a volume put together by Brian Ford. The biggest disaster was our first meeting after poster announcements were no longer carried by *Biologist.* Our small entry in the new *Biobits* was spectacularly ineffective, resulting in a few committee members occupying a hall for 200 and a huge sponsored buffet that went to the poor folk under the bridge. (The next Branch Secretaries' meeting at HQ was a less than friendly affair.)

It is likely that our Branch was labelled as wild activists in the mid-1990s, when we sensed a determined effort to disband the Branches on the grounds of cost. As we pointed out, the costs amounted to three per cent of the subscription income. Like other Branches, we were so angered that a huge file of correspondence now exists and a growing sense of fraternity developed among Branch Secretaries. This came to a head in one particularly memorable meeting with a few officers and the rather surprised new President of the Institute, after which it was decreed that Branch meetings were to be cancelled and funds would not be provided for Branch representatives to attend the AGMs. 'Perhaps it is all a smoke screen set up to avoid anyone looking more closely at where the money was really going,' some even said!

In due course there was a clean sweep at HQ and it is a great credit to those in control that the situation could be so much improved. Relationships now can be described as excellent. We carefully plan Branch expenditure in line with the aims of the Institute, submit it on time, and never have any arguments, largely thanks to the post of Branches Co-ordinator, established by Eric Carter. Branch representatives attend six-monthly meetings and report that suggestions have been accepted. Working parties have tackled particular issues, such as the way the Branches are presented in *Biobits*. We can indeed see progress.

Everyone on the committee takes a turn in organising meetings, adding variety and interest, such as a castle boat trip down the River Trent, *At the cutting edge of dentistry* (where light is used on teeth instead of a drill), fungal forays, whales, environmental law in biotechnology today, new-wave diseases, genetics and food. We run an annual Award for Biological Excellence, photographic competitions, a *Who's who in the East Midlands* and careers fairs. We support around 750 members spread over 100 000 km^2 over five counties. We have good relationships with high-powered, jet-setting biologists in industry as well as the illustrious biologists in the world of academia and the more modest enthusiasts, some of whom have been tempted into biology from other walks of life.

To communicate with members nowadays, we have found our website and mass e-mail list useful, although people are changing their addresses with remarkable frequency. Even today, nothing beats the response from the old pony express of direct mail — licked envelopes and all. Attendances are a little up, as is membership, and we have a keen committee with a regular turnover (of Chairmen, at any rate) as well as some stalwarts who provide the continuity of friendly faces to greet and talk with members. New blood is successfully hounded in and Branch funds put to good use, which all helps to promote biology in our society today. **"**

INTO THE EIGHTIES

C U M Smith FRSA PhD CBiol FIBiol
Honorary Visiting Fellow in Vision Sciences, Aston University

Seven months before the 1980s began, a radical Prime Minister at the head of a reforming Government had been elected into office. This event was to have far-reaching consequences for the whole of the United Kingdom, including the profession of biology and its mouthpiece, the Institute of Biology. Very soon a harsh wind was gathering, ready to blow through the complacencies and received wisdoms of the post-war settlement. Not only the trade unions but also the professions found themselves exposed to critical appraisal. What purpose did they serve? Were they delivering value for money? Why should they expect support from the hard-pressed taxpayer?

Charter celebrations

We could only speculate on how many of the guests at a gathering of the great and the good at the Natural History Museum in South Kensington on 24 January 1980 were aware of the oncoming shake-out. This glittering occasion marked a double celebration: first, it was a celebration to mark the 30th anniversary of the Institute's foundation and, second, a celebration to mark the receipt of a Royal Charter from

Her Majesty the Queen 'to advance the science and practice of biology and its application, to advance education therein, and to co-ordinate and encourage the study of biology and its application'. Sir Michael Swann, Chairman of the Governors of the BBC, was our guest of honour. Among the other distinguished guests were Mr and Mrs David Attenborough, the Chairman of the Biological Council, Professor and Mrs Cloudsley-Thompson, Sir Bernard and Lady Katz, Professor and Mrs Mellanby, Lord Rothschild, Dame Margaret Weston (Director of the Science Museum), and many other of the influential individuals of that period. A special issue of *Biologist* was

Charter Award: 'Life form'.

published to celebrate this significant *rite de passage* in the Institute's existence and an annual Charter Award was instituted. This award, a green-tinted bronze maquette sculpted by John Farnham and entitled 'Life form', was to be presented at the Institute's AGM to a member of the Institute who had made an outstanding contribution to the work of the biological community within the United Kingdom. The newly chartered Institute was being given a memorable send-off on its voyage into what were to prove increasingly stormy waters.

Financial cuts

The first indication in the Institute's minutes of heavy weather ahead came at a meeting of the officers on 3 December 1980. Here they considered, among other things, the output of graduate biologists from the country's universities and colleges. This was done in the light of a quotation from Sir Geoffrey Allen (a physical chemist and industrialist) in the *Times Higher Education Supplement:* 'Look at the rise of biology. No Prime Minister said that this was the thing to do yet the kids are all taking biology. The biochemistry and biology courses in universities are full to overflowing. We train far too many postgraduate biologists.' With the benefit of hindsight, a knowledge of late 20th-century developments in biotechnology, a familiarity with the environmental concerns of the end of the century (not least GM foods), and a recognition of the revolution in human self-understanding which the genome project and reproductive technologies are now bringing us, perhaps 'the kids', rather than Sir Geoffrey, were right. But at the beginning of the 1980s such insights were possessed by few people in positions of authority. Also before the meeting was a report from a working party at the University of Southampton containing the statement: 'The UGC indicated that it thinks far too many biologists are graduating' and, furthermore, a member of the UGC, darkly suspected of being a computer scientist, had suggested that the current overproduction of graduates in the biological sciences (taking all the universities together) might be a factor to be considered 'in the forthcoming financial settlement'.

In the light of these disturbing comments, the Institute prepared a questionnaire and distributed it to all heads of departments in universities and colleges who were running undergraduate courses in biological sciences (broadly conceived). The response to this questionnaire did little to help the cause. It suggested that 'just over' 400 biologists graduated each year who might be 'surplus to requirement'. It was also calculated that over the decade 1968/9 to 1978/9 the numbers graduating in biology had grown by 42 per cent, while those in chemistry had declined by 28 per cent and in physics by 10 per cent. Storm clouds gathered yet more visibly when the *Financial Times*, on 19 February 1981, published an article suggesting that the number of experienced biologists unemployed between October 1980 and February 1981 had increased by 106. This gloomy news was picked up and broadcast by the

BBC *Today* programme on 20 February 1981, where it was exaggeratedly reported that the number of unemployed biologists had increased by 'over 100 per cent' in the last four months. An article in *Biologist* of June 1981 reviewed the statistics of staff and student numbers in university biology departments and examined employment prospects and funding provisions. The UGC financial settlement and advice was published the following month.

The full story of the politics behind the radical financial cuts in university finance of July 1981 has yet to be told. It is strange that an administration devoted to market solutions to economic problems should have sought to predict the future and impose manpower planning. Nevertheless, this is what happened. The intention of the UGC settlement of July 1981 was to reduce the total number of UK students by five per cent over the triennium 1981–84 and to reduce the recurrent grant by 11 – 15 per cent (variance: 0 – 35 per cent). Within this overall settlement the cuts in biological science were going to be swingeing. A first circular stated that, in general, 'new developments in biological sciences should be supported, including those with high potential value for the economy, to some extent at the expense of other aspects of biology, and numbers overall may fall slightly'. A second circular came down to specifics. In seeming contradiction to the first circular, it recommended cataclysmic cuts in those departments that had sought to develop the applied aspects of biology. It was recommended that biology should be eliminated altogether at Bradford and Aston, substantially reduced at Brunel and Salford, and that phasing out should be discussed at Essex. Commenting on these outcomes, Beardmore and Copp (1981) concluded that 'for the biological sciences as a whole it appears that the effects of these reductions in grant and student numbers will be both unpleasant and unnecessarily damaging'.

As we have seen, in spite of some early controversies, the Institute was never in the position of a trade union arguing for the terms of employment and against involuntary redundancy of biologists. Nevertheless the Institute kept a watching brief over the 'unpleasant and ... damaging' consequences of the 1981 UGC settlement, which had at first seemed to threaten the livelihoods of between 150 and 350 academic staff. Agenda items recur through the 1980s referring to struggles of academic biologists to rebalance their teaching and research enterprises in the more hostile environment of year-on-year cuts in public funding and so-called efficiency savings.

Changes in secondary education

It was not, of course, only in tertiary education that great changes were under way in the 1980s. The Education Division, since its formation in 1976, had been closely involved in monitoring the changes proposed for biological education in secondary schools. There was a general feeling that the English educational system forced premature specialisation onto its pupils. It was customary for post-GCSE students to be forced to choose between the arts and the sciences, and very common for choices to be further enforced within the sciences themselves. Students aiming to study physics, chemistry or mathematics at university seldom saw fit to study biology in the sixth form. Ever since the 1970s there has been a move to erase biology from the spectrum of A-level subjects studied by those hoping to enter medical school. As medicine is a career to which many studying A-level biology in sixth forms and elsewhere aspire, the Institute was justifiably concerned. A symposium on the issue had been held in 1977, and in February 1988 the Biomedical and Education Divisions, in conjunction with the Association for the Study of Medical Education, organised a successful conference at the Institute of Education in London to discuss the problem once again.

Early specialisation in schools was driven by university admissions tutors, who demanded that freshers should immediately be able to cope with an advanced scientific curriculum. The archives of the Institute (notably in April 1986) reveal the level of concern at the difficulties young people were experiencing at the interface between school and university. The demand for expertly prepared first-year students is, of course, due to the comparatively short duration of English undergraduate degree courses. It was imperative to start with well-qualified freshers if the honours degree was to qualify students to begin research on the frontiers of science. Following the train of cause-and-effect back to its source we find, as ever, the Treasury. Longer university undergraduate courses inevitably cost more, and the purse strings were drawn tightly against any further disbursement of public money to the universities and colleges. The outcome of this chain of events was, many felt, an intellectual narrowness, an inability to cross what came to be known as the 'Snow-line', the division postulated between the arts and science-minded disciplines.

Many attempts to broaden secondary education were being made during the 1980s: integrated science and double-award balanced science at the GCSE level, together with AS levels in the sixth form. Some of these attempts, for instance double-award balanced science, generated a great deal of work, up to and including the writing (though not the publication) of textbooks, but they ultimately foundered. The biological content of these new attempts at a syllabus exercised the minds of members of the Education Division as we moved towards the mid-1980s. It was often felt that the mandarins in the DES had little feel for the quantity (and cost) of the teacher retraining necessary if these integrated syllabuses were to be more than a hotchpotch of poorly related modules. In the event it has to be said that, with the exception of the AS levels (which never gained wide acceptance), few of these initiatives stood the test of time and practical implementation. A-levels remained the gold standard to which the school syllabus was ultimately orientated. The problem of broadening the secondary curriculum and allowing post-GCSE pupils insight into both sides of C P Snow's 'two cultures' was not solved in the 1980s and, indeed, has not been solved since. It seems likely that, unless new funding becomes available, even the developments of this new millennium will fail to find a solution to this intractable problem.

The Institute and secondary education

During this decade, the Institute was frequently being called upon to adjudicate over more specific issues relating to secondary education. The diversity of biology ensured that these matters were many and various. In September 1983, for instance, the Institute was asked to respond to concerns about the use of living organisms in schools. Over the decade, not only the use of living organisms but also the dissection of dead specimens began to be phased out of the curriculum. The Institute, on the whole, condoned this move, suggesting that pupils should be directed to study syllabuses from those examination boards that did not require such practical experience. In March 1984 a joint document on the use of animals in schools (produced with the Association of Science Education) was issued. It recommended that dissection in schools should be made into an optional subject. What the 19th-century founders of biological education in England, Thomas Henry Huxley in particular, whose dominating portrait hangs in the Institute's committee room, would have made of this must be left to the imagination. Then in July 1985 the Institute considered a DES discussion document on homework. It broadly supported the document with the proviso that homework should not be over-specified and that variety should always be emphasised.

The significance of the computer revolution was also recognised. A workshop on *Computers in schools* was organised in March 1986 and a short report with the same title was published. In the event, the DES was prevailed upon to send a copy to every secondary school in the maintained sector. Another issue upon which the Institute pronounced, after consultation with the BMA, was that of teaching about AIDs in schools (February 1987). Twentieth-century mass media, especially television, frequently reveal how biology, and especially biomedicine, reaches deep into human life. Schoolchildren look to their teachers, and their teachers often look to the Institute for authoritative and considered comment. With this kind of topic in mind, in 1987 the Institute launched a Schools Affiliation Scheme. This received financial support from a small number of chiefly pharmaceutical companies. Schools belonging to this scheme received a specially produced periodical called *Offshoots*. This mainly contained tips and hints for sixth-form teachers, but although enthusiastically edited and much appreciated it was not destined to be a permanent feature of the Institute's publication portfolio. None the less, more than 200 schools and colleges had affiliated under this scheme before the end of the decade.

A final, valuable contribution to secondary education was the publication of a booklet covering nomenclature, units, and symbols for biology courses in secondary education. This was the outcome of a working party set up by the Institute under the chairmanship of Wilf Stout of the University of Cambridge Local Examinations Syndicate, with representatives from the schools and colleges. A draft report was circulated in May 1987 to over 700 interested parties and, in the light of their responses, a booklet containing draft recommendations was published in January 1988. These recommendations attempted to standardise not only biological systematics but also the terms and symbols used in biochemistry, genetics, and animal and plant physiology. The Institute of Biology has always been in a unique position to initiate such wide-ranging reviews; no other body has an overview of all the biological specialities. This unique position was also the basis for proposals made by our 1987 President, Sir Kenneth Blaxter, to develop a 'centre for biology' *(vide infra)*.

Higher National Certificates and Diplomas

In addition to school and university biology, the Institute was also concerned with HNC and HND in Applied Biology. These syllabuses were followed in many polytechnics, technical colleges and colleges of further education, and C G C Chesters chaired a joint biology committee which oversaw and moderated this work. These awards were discontinued in the early 1980s and the last examinations, except for a small number of resits, were held in the summer of 1981. They were to be replaced by TEC qualifications. The joint committee was wound up in 1983, and Chesters chaired the final meeting, having been its first and only chairman, thereby completing 30 years of work for the Institute. The loss of fees for the HNC/HND in Applied Biology and the move away from GIBiol by examination to CNAA awards in colleges and polytechnics resulted in quite a serious loss of income to the Institute. It has been computed that the income stream was depleted by £70 000 – £80 000 per annum — a very considerable sum. Similar changes were proceeding in Scotland, and in 1987 the Institute reviewed and provided supportive comment on a consultative paper from SCOTVEC (the Scottish Vocational Education Council) which proposed a system of further education qualifications more flexibly tailored to the changing needs of industry and commerce.

New accommodation

One item that figured largely in the early 1980s was the physical location of the Institute's headquarters. In its early years, as we have seen, the Institute had made use of rented premises, latterly in the Queen's Gate building of the Royal Entomological Society. Although excellent relations obtained with the entomologists, rented accommodation offered no permanent solution for a major scientific body. Various options had been canvassed, including a move out of expensive and congested London altogether. In the late 1970s a fund had been established to purchase permanent accommodation. On 31 August 1981 the minutes of the Institute record that a property in South Kensington might become available. This referred to the mention by A C Mohan that a secretarial college was moving out of 20 Queensberry Place. The minutes of several subsequent meetings record ongoing discussion of the possibility of purchasing this property. In 1982 negotiations were completed and the Institute purchased the property for use as a new headquarters for the sum of £282 900. Although the financial negotiations were long drawn out and complex, the move itself was lightning swift. It is reported that not a single day's work was lost in the transfer, which must be some sort of record.

The history of Queensberry Place is bound up with the Great Exhibition of 1851. Before that date the area had consisted largely of market gardens supplying early Victorian London. After the Exhibition ended, the Exhibition Commission, under their President, Prince Albert, purchased 87 acres of this open space with a view to constructing museums and other cultural centres. Later, in 1857, it was realised that too much land had been sequestered for these purposes and the area on which the headquarters of the Institute now stands was sold for speculative building development. A Scotsman, William Douglas, saw the potential, bought some of the land, and in the 1860s and 1870s laid out Queensberry Place (see Wylson, 1983). The name derives from a mountain in Douglas' native Dumfriesshire. Records show that in 1881 number 20 was occupied by a typical Victorian family, one Dr Kennedy, a widower, with two daughters, two elderly sisters, a daughter-in-law, and a grandson. The domestic staff included a coachman, cook, two housemaids, a parlourmaid and a lady's maid. The accommodation into which the Institute moved on Tuesday 15 February 1983 still bore marks of this comfortable Victorian establishment. Considerable refurbishment was essential before it could be used as office accommodation. The dining room at the front was initially converted into a council room, the kitchen at the back became a staff common room, and the servants' hall in the front became the print room and stationery store. The upper rooms which had served as nurseries, dressing rooms, and bedrooms became administrative offices, while the 12 vaults under the pavement, which had probably been wine cellars, found themselves converted into the less convivial role of storage space for the Institute's files and papers.

The rapidity of the Institute's move from Queen's Gate to Queensberry Place was more than somewhat vitiated by the scale of the reconstruction and refurbishment needed, and by the ineptitude of the company responsible. Much work had to be done to meet fire and sanitary regulations as well as to convert what was still essentially a family house into the headquarters of a scientific organisation. The officers and staff of the Institute had to make do and mend within a building in the throes of an inefficient remodelling. This, compounded by continuous financial stringency, made life at the centre less glamorous than has sometimes been imagined by those on the fringe. The issue of the Institute's headquarters was, moreover, not settled by

20 – 22 Queensberry Place, London SW7, current home of the Institute.

the move to 20 Queensberry Place. It was understandably felt that the rooms were too small and the building too cramped (with 3940 square feet of usable space) to allow expansion. The Institute's minutes record an ongoing search for larger premises throughout the remainder of the decade.

Staff changes at Queensberry Place

During this period in the early 1980s significant changes occurred in the staffing at the London headquarters. In 1982 Dax Copp OBE left our service after 30 years as General Secretary of the Institute. His outstanding contribution was marked by the award of Honorary Fellowship (the Institute's highest award) in 1984. During the following year, the Dax Copp Travelling Fellowship was inaugurated to create 'an opportunity for travel in connection with biological study or research to teachers and others who would (otherwise) be unlikely to do so'. A sum of about £1000 is available every two years.

Copp was succeeded in the post of General Secretary by Philip O'Donoghue who, as we have seen, served as Honorary Secretary from 1972–76. O'Donoghue thus oversaw the final phases of the negotiation for the new Queensberry Place headquarters and supervised the removals. As he says, when an organisation has a staff as small as that of the Institute, personalities become unusually significant — he adds that the Institute has been 'extremely fortunate in how few bad apples, and how many talented and dedicated staff' have served over the years. He pays generous tribute to Copp's role in seizing every opportunity to build a secure position within the British scientific establishment for the Institute. Staffing continued to prove a contentious issue throughout the mid-1980s. In the end O'Donoghue decided to leave in 1988 and Robert Priestley was appointed to succeed him as General Secretary.

Unifying the diversity

The Institute's Royal Charter states that the term 'biology' includes 'all aspects of the science of living matter'. The Institute's remit thus covers a vast range of disciplines and subdisciplines. Biology, far more than physics and chemistry, is a highly

Three General Secretaries of the Institute: (l to r) Phil O'Donohue, Dax Copp, Robert Priestley.

diverse and subdivided subject. This is both a strength and a weakness. It is a strength in that it allows specialisation in an individual area and hence depth, but a weakness in that its practitioners often lose touch with the centre and feel loyalty first to their speciality and only second to biology as a whole. Physiologists, for instance, look first to fellow physiologists and the Physiological Society (which significantly predates the Institute), microbiologists confer primarily with other microbiologists, geneticists with geneticists, entomologists with entomologists, and so on. The Institute was well aware of this diversity and towards the end of the 1980s sought to bring the multitudinous specialised societies under the umbrella of the Institute in the form of affiliates.

Centre for Biology

A yet more powerful initiative to bring about a reconciliation of diverse biological interests took the form of a proposal that was mooted in 1987 by the then President, Sir Kenneth Blaxter. He proposed the establishment of a Centre for Biological Societies — a true 'centre for British biology'. This idea, as previous chapters have shown, was not new. It had been much in the minds of the founding fathers of the Institute and reappears throughout its 50-year history, but it received a particularly powerful boost in the late 1980s. After a considerable period of gestation at Queensberry Place, Sir Kenneth — accompanied by the principal officers of the Institute — introduced his concept to the representatives of some 40 biological societies at a meeting in December 1987 held at the Polytechnic of Central London. Biology, he pointed out, had grown since its beginnings in the 19th century into an overly fragmented subject, especially when compared with physics or chemistry. Nevertheless, there was considerable overlap between the biological specialities, and considerable common interest. Yet there remained no single centre where speciality could talk to speciality, where the forces of reintegration could gather strength, and no single body that could speak with an authoritative voice for the common interest. What was needed, Sir Kenneth argued, was some central locale in which the diverse special societies could come together for committee meetings, which could provide common secretarial and publishing facilities, and where different specialists could meet and talk. While the Institute would manage the Centre (without in any way infringing the autonomy of the various societies), its own building in Queensberry Place was too cramped for such an ambitious undertaking. On the other hand, it was recognised that the Queensberry Place building in South Kensington, although con-stricted, was now very valuable. Could its value be realised and spent on some more commodious accommodation? Should an appeal for funds be launched? Various possibilities were investigated. A consultancy firm was asked to investigate the possi-bilities of an appeal for funds. Discussions with the Wellcome Trust about sharing its buildings in the Euston Road were initiated and sites in the provinces, including the University of York, considered. In the event, the 1980s were to end without the issue being resolved.

The Divisions

The 1980s saw continued development of the four specialised Divisions that had been established in the mid-1970s: Agricultural Sciences, Biomedical Sciences, Education and Environment. These Divisions had been set up to provide for 'the professional and scientific needs of biologists practising in these fields by holding meetings on relevant topics and by making policy statements via the Council of the Institute' (Anon, 1980). Each Division was to be run by a committee chaired by a distinguished biologist and, to prevent the tendency for subdivision mentioned above, each Chairman reported to the Council of the Institute. At the beginning of the 1980s the Chairmen were Sir Colin Spedding (Agricultural Sciences), Desmond Hammerton (Environment), R J Terry (Biomedical Sciences) and G E Beedham (Education). Each Division chose top-ics of current concern to which to devote their energies. In 1986 Council was informed that the four Divisions had decided on topics for attention. The Agricultural Sciences Division selected nutrition; the Biomedical Sciences Division proposed a conference on the consequences of the Chernobyl disaster (*vide infra*) and also to investigate the possibility of a register of scientists in healthcare; the Education Division was heavily involved with the relationship of A-levels and GCSE examinations and also the fund-ing of science libraries and the standardisation of biological nomenclature; while the

Environment Division intended to provide 'rapid responses' to environmental impacts of onshore oil exploration, the privatisation of water supplies, the use of pesticides, and Eurotunnel.

Members of the Institute could belong to one or at most two Divisions and their interests were recorded on a pioneering computer database. This database was expanded in June 1987 when a large questionnaire surveying professional interests was circulated to the membership. The questions covered the nature of work being done, type of employer, biological interests and specialisations. The resulting computer database proved to be of considerable use in tailoring meetings, visits and other events to the interests of the local membership.

A miscellany of interests

Although the concerns of biologists in education invariably loomed large in the Institute's debates, many other interests occupied its time and energies. In May 1985 the Institute commented on the 1985–90 corporate plan of the NERC. This plan was of considerable interest to the Institute, of course, which found it to be highly disappointing. In particular, the Institute noted that, although a great deal of attention had been devoted to the management and organisation of the NERC headquarters, comparatively little space had been devoted to the scientific work of the Council. The Institute felt that the Council should set out its scientific targets for the short- and long-term future rather than navel-gaze at its office organisation. When NERC replied, they stated that the Institute had misunderstood the aims and objects of the corporate plan.

In September that year a member wrote requesting financial support for maintaining the greenhouse at Down House, formerly the home of Charles Darwin. He pointed out that it was in a state of sad disrepair and that a small amount of financial assistance could see it converted into a fitting memorial to Darwin's work on plants. It says something about the financial pressures under which the Institute worked that this request was regretfully turned down. Later that year the Institute considered a discussion paper on policy for broad-leaved woodlands in Britain, and interest in this area is maintained in several subsequent sets of minutes of the Institute's meetings. In October 1986 a report of work with the Department of the Environment on whelk populations was considered. Then, in December of the same year, the topic of admissions charges to the Natural History Museum was discussed and commented upon. Also in 1986 the Institute submitted a response to a document entitled *The policy and practice of public support for civil science and technology within the United Kingdom*, circulated by Government's select committee on science and technology. The Institute argued strongly for 'a strong spine of civil research, technology and teaching' and, moreover, for a stable long-term plan to provide tenure and career security.

In January 1987 the Institute submitted a report on freshwater quality to the Royal Commission on Environmental Pollution, and in April a response to a consultative document on pesticide residues was sent to MAFF. It is interesting also to note that in November 1989 the Institute published an informed commentary on the pros and cons of genetically modified organisms (GMOs), a topic which was to assume major political importance a decade later. This small selection of the topics reviewed and decided upon at our headquarters in Queensberry Place exemplifies the great variety of matters, from small to large, from scientific to administrative and commercial, which by this time were falling within the remit of an Institute that saw itself devoted to the whole of biology.

Branch activity

The Institute is more than its metropolitan base. More often than not, our Branches are where the action is. Thus the glittering occasion in 1980 at the Natural History Museum to mark the granting of our Royal Charter 'to advance the science and practice of biology' was far from being the only celebration. Enthusiastically supported events were held throughout the United Kingdom (Anon, 1981). Several Branches instituted an annual Charter Lecture to commemorate the event. Many celebrated with gatherings in which the biology of food and drink figured largely. The Yorkshire Branch, for instance, mounted a lecture on the biology of cheese and wine, while the North Western Branch, not to be outdone by their colleagues across the Pennines, set up a talk on wine-tasting in the cellars of Owens of Wilmslow. Other events ranged from an evening when the Marquess of Bute addressed the Scottish Branch in the Edinburgh headquarters of the Royal Zoological Society of Scotland, to a visit by one Charles Darwin Esquire who provided some historical gravitas to a meeting of the East Anglia Branch. The activities of the Branches are many and varied and primarily designed to satisfy local needs. Nevertheless, it was felt in Queensberry Place that at least their organisation should be unified. Thus it was that in 1985 a new constitutional document was approved by Council which regularised their operation in terms of election of officers, terms of service, structure of committees, appointment of auditors, etc.

Membership matters

Membership of the Institute was kept under review throughout the 1980s and was often a cause for concern. Membership rose from 14 464 in 1980 to a peak of 16 332 in 1984 before losing over a thousand members and falling back to 15 239 at the end of the decade. Even at its highest the membership probably included no more than about a third of the UK's qualified biologists. Various stratagems were attempted to increase the numbers. Some of them — school affiliations, raising the significance of chartered status, etc — are referred to in other parts of this chapter. A survey of all independent schools was undertaken in 1986 with a view to identifying heads of all the biology departments which included sixth forms. Although 200 schools were identified and their biology staff invited to apply for Institute membership, very few (no more than half a dozen) in fact did so. Then in April 1987 the Institute wrote to heads of biological departments in all the UK's universities and polytechnics, enclosing a package of recruitment literature. It is not recorded how successful this initiative proved to be. The Institute's archives still contain numerous letters from throughout the 1980s relating to changes of address and the search for members of the Institute with whom contact had been lost. The advent of improved computer facilities, e-mail and the Internet in recent years should make this task less onerous.

One very important development in the mid-1980s did, however, make membership of the Institute far more significant. This was the agreement by the Privy Council in July 1984 that Fellows and Members of the Institute should have the status of Chartered Biologist, CBiol. Such status, according to the Privy Council rubric, provides 'evidence that a biologist's professional qualifications and experience have been approved by his peers and is a definite measure of knowledge and ability'. Chartered status has not only become important in the context of the European Union, but also brings the profession of biology into line with those of chemistry, physics and engineering.

Although, as we have seen, the Institute was in no sense a trade union it nevertheless very properly concerned itself with the pay scales of its Fellows, Members, Graduates and Associates. To this end a questionnaire on remuneration was sent out in February 1980. Responses came from about one-third of the entire membership, with 3358 replies from a possible 10 500, and the resulting statistics make interesting reading. They showed, in particular, that over a three-year period, members of the Institute below the age of 45 were already beginning to slip behind the rise in the cost of living. Whereas the retail price index had increased by 43 per cent over the triennium 1977–80, remuneration of these younger biologists had only increased from 27 to 32 per cent. It was also noticeable that, on average, biologists were faring less well in the salary stakes than their chemist and physicist colleagues. This disparity, as was pointed out in a *New Scientist* report on 24 April 1980, may have been partly due to more physicists and chemists working in industry than biologists. Nevertheless this slippage in the remuneration of qualified biologists can perhaps be seen as a straw in the wind, pointing to a continuing erosion as the century entered its last two decades. The Institute, representing as it does the broad community of biologists, can and does play a significant role in bringing this deterioration to the notice of paymasters in Government and elsewhere.

European Union

A further and increasingly important role that the Institute plays as the 'voice of British biology' has to do with Europe. In the early 1980s, at the prompting of the General Secretary, the Institute was recognised by the Department of Trade and Industry as the appropriate body to negotiate academic equivalence with biologists in other European Union states. In 1983 O'Donoghue, then our General Secretary, chaired the first meeting of the European Communities Biological Association (ECBA) at Abano in Italy. This inaugural meeting led to a large number of subsequent meetings in which attempts (ultimately successful) were made to harmonise biological qualifications across the EU. The PhD was, for instance, equated with the French *troisième cycle*. In 1989, at the instigation of the Institute, the CIBA Foundation sponsored a meeting at which prominent biologists and others were invited to discuss professional matters affecting biologists across the EU. Amongst the distinguished guests at this meeting was the Head of the Directorate-General XII, Paolo Fasella, who was responsible for the co-ordination of scientific research funded throughout the Community. Eventually, CBiol, became recognised as the professional qualification for biologists throughout the Community and its holders were invited to apply for the designatory letters EurBiol, indicating a EU-wide recognition of biological excellence. It seems likely that these moves, started in the 1980s, will greatly assist the mobility of biologists across an expanded EU in the 21st century.

A strategy for higher education

In the mid-1980s the UGC was in the throes of developing a strategy for higher education in the 1990s. In March 1980 the Institute was asked to submit a paper to its biological sciences subcommittee. The Institute emphasised three significant growth points: biotechnology, molecular biology and ecology. In retrospect the Institute was not far wrong although, with the 1990s being designated by the US President as the 'decade of the brain', perhaps some reference should have been made to neuroscience. Another question asked by the UGC at this time referred to selectivity in research funding. This was the first hint of the periodic research selectivity or assessment exercises (RAEs) which were to loom large in the work of universities in the late eighties and throughout the nineties. Once again the causal chain can be traced back to the Treasury. With the ever-increasing number of university departments involved in research, especially after the total number of universities was roughly doubled by the redesignation of the polytechnics in 1992, and with the increasing cost of world-class research, it became impossible to support all the 'well-found' facilities throughout the sector. It was concluded that research had to be concentrated in a small number of centres of excellence. The periodic RAEs were designed to find where these nodes of outstanding research were located. The Biblical injunction was then to be invoked: to those that have shall be given, and to those that have not shall be taken away even that which they have. The initial response of the Institute in 1984 was that the idea of selectivity in the distribution of research funding was 'extremely dangerous'. The Institute correctly saw that one of the outcomes of the RAE regime would be to unbalance the universities. Without a research presence, a university department would find it hard to attract new academic staff, without fresh research staff the students would look elsewhere for their tertiary education, and ultimately the department would wither on the vine. Many universities would consequently lose the comprehensive range of academic departments which, it was widely felt, justified the name 'university'. Naturally, the Treasury view prevailed. Its consequences are still unfolding.

Public understanding

Yet another major involvement of the Institute in the 1980s was with the public understanding of science (PUS). In the late 20th century science became an enormously expensive undertaking. Gone are the days of the dilettante, of the simple microscope, and of sealing wax and string. Instead huge laboratories filled with complex equipment, staffed by highly trained acolytes, churn out results which fill a myriad of scientific journals. This costs money, and money in such quantities that it can only come from the taxpayer. Why should this overburdened individual continue to pay, especially when so many other seemingly more worthy causes compete for his or her hard-earned contribution? Why, even more pressingly, should the taxpayer continue to support a profession which, what with nuclear bombs and pollution, chemical warfare, genetically modified foods, ecodisasters, and catastrophes like nvCJD, not to mention the whole animal rights movement, finds itself ever more demonised? There is a clear necessity for a better understanding of science, its benefits and *raison d'être*. As early as July 1983 the Institute was asked to submit its views on this issue, which grows in importance and recurs in the minutes of the Institute throughout the 1980s and into the next decade. In 1986, for instance, the Institute wrote to the Royal Society, the lead organisation in the PUS, indicating its interest and willingness to undertake work to further the public understanding of biology.

Associated with the Institute's participation in the PUS was its involvement with the British Association for the Advancement of Science (BA). This organisation, dating back to the 1830s, acts as the major channel for the popularisation of science in the UK. It has sister organisations in many other parts of the English-speaking world. The BA's major contribution is its annual festival of science, held each year in September at different universities in the UK. Many members of the Institute speak at these conferences, explaining their science to the scientifically interested general public, but in the 1980s one- or two-day meetings were instituted within these week-long annual festivals. These conferences were known as Mason conferences, after their instigator, Sir Ronald Mason, President of the BA in the early eighties. In 1986 one of the first of these Mason conferences was sponsored by the Institute of Biology. It was entitled *Biology and industry*, and was jointly chaired by I Graham-Bryce of Shell International and J M Lynch of the Glasshouse Research Institute. This two-day meeting at the University of Bristol attracted 'warm support' and was attended by about 35 senior people from industry, education and the public services. A report of this meeting was circulated to Government departments, industry and local education authorities and published in *Biologist*. Far less successful was a meeting organised by the Biomedical Sciences Division in 1986 on the biological consequences of the Chernobyl disaster. The meeting was held on 11 April 1987 at the Royal College of Surgeons of England (RCS). In addition to speakers from the Central Electricity Generating Board and from Moscow, we also welcomed Dr R Gale from Los Angeles, H D Roeder from West Germany, and T Hugosson from Sweden. Nevertheless, somewhat mystifyingly to Stuart Roath, the organiser, and his team, it attracted no more than 80 delegates. This 'spectacularly low' attendance for such a topical meeting left embarrassingly large empty spaces in the RCS lecture room. The reasons for this poor attendance were never made clear, but the Institute ended with a £6000 loss.

The History Group

In a volume dedicated to the history of the Institute of Biology it is only to be expected that mention should be made of the inauguration of a History Group, which has since become the History Network (and has been responsible for the writing of this book). A note published by Nick Russell in the September 1985 *Biologist* asked all those interested in the history of biology to make contact, and a small group of enthusiasts met at Queensberry Place in December 1985. It was agreed to go ahead with the formation of a Group and a series of meetings ensued. Early meetings were held at Queensberry Place and in the rooms of the Royal Entomological Society in Queen's Gate. The Group began production of a duplicated newsletter, *Biology History*, which eventually ran to 18 issues spanning eight years.

Publications

Biology History never became an official part of the Institute's publishing activities. Far more important from the Institute's point of view have been *Biologist* and the *Journal of Biological Education (JBE)*. The style and frequency of publication of these journals were the cause of much agonising throughout the 1980s. Many complaints about the tardiness of publication and distribution of *Biologist* are to be found in letters and minutes preserved in the archives. The publications committee, under the chairmanship of Jack Cohen and then Jack Hannay, sought to improve the punctuality, the look and hence the impact of both journals, but their efforts were

Cover of an issue of Biology History. *This one contained the proceedings of one of the History Committee's symposia.*

continually hamstrung through lack of funds.

In addition to these two flagship publications the Institute continued to involve itself in the very successful series of small books, *Studies in Biology*, published by Edward Arnold, and later also in *Modern Views of Biology* (Allen and Unwin) and *Biotechnology* (Oxford University Press). The Institute's symposia proceedings also frequently found a publisher. A particularly interesting case was the March 1988 symposium organised by the Agricultural Sciences and Environment Divisions *Since* Silent Spring: *an update on the ecological effects of agricultural pesticides in the UK*. In his summarising comment at the end of this symposium John Bowman, the then Secretary of the NERC, queried whether reasonable progress had been made in the 26 years since Rachel Carson published *Silent Spring*, and admitted to disappointment in finding that the use of 'bio-biocides' was driven more by commercial than scientific interests. Other publications by the Institute were *Offshoots* (mentioned above) and a periodically updated *Careers in Biology*.

In the summer of 1985 the publications committee investigated the possibility of publishing computer software of biological interest, and a computer club for Institute members was also mooted. The Institute felt, however, that its limited resources should be concentrated on upgrading and developing *Biologist* and the *JBE*. *Biologist* appeared in a new format in 1989 and has subsequently gone through further guises and face-lifts and is now, at the time of writing, a far more attractive publication. It serves a valuable function not only in printing authoritative articles written in such a way that they are accessible to a wide spectrum of biologists, but also in publicising news of events mounted by the Branches and general developments, such as EurBiol, of interest to all members of the Institute.

Conclusions

In conclusion, can we pick out any major themes running through the Institute's work in the 1980s? Perhaps the major ongoing concern was, very properly, the education and training of biologists. The Institute, having no financial leverage, was in a weak position to influence events which, as we have seen, were ultimately driven by the Treasury. Nevertheless its advice was sought and freely given and, no doubt, had some influence on the decisions taken. Another, related, theme was the continuous financial exigency in which the Institute found itself. Compared with the other scientific and engineering institutes, the Institute of Biology remained very much the poor relation. That it was not ultimately a country cousin was due to the luck and good judgement of Messrs Mohan and O'Donoghue in securing our headquarters within five minutes' walk of the major biological resource in the UK, the South Kensington Natural History Museum. A third theme was the gradual enhancement in the value of the chartered status enshrined in the letters CBiol. As the decade drew to its close this status achieved EU-wide recognition as a prerequisite for the EurBiol qualification. Looking back over the decade of the 1980s, the major impression is that of the sheer variety and extent of work with which the Institute was involved. It ranged from surveys of littoral whelk populations to comments on university research assessment exercises, from publishing journals to advising on school homework, from active involvement in the public understanding of science to investigating and advising on the pay scales of biologists.

In 1988 an ambitious document, *Development Plan 1988–90 and on to 2000 AD*, was approved by Council. This included many of the issues touched on in this chapter: fostering the unity of biology, public understanding of biology, biological issues of public concern, improving contacts with industry, education, qualifications, publications, improving communications within the Institute, and, of course, recruitment. The plan established a framework within which it was proposed that the Institute and its work should develop into the next decade. In the event some areas (e.g. EU-wide qualification) developed faster than others (e.g. a Centre for Biology). The lasting impression from the survey of the Institute in the 1980s given in this chapter is that of a youthful organisation struggling to find its feet, struggling to find its way, and emerging from the cold winds of the 1980s stronger and perhaps even more ambitious than when it began.

Officers of the eighties

Leadership makes a difference. Throughout the 1980s the Institute was fortunate in attracting outstanding individuals to its honorary positions of President, Honorary Secretary, and Honorary Treasurer. The list of Presidents includes many of the leading names in British biology.

Ernest Barrington (President 1980–81) began his career as an organ scholar at Oriel College, Oxford. His interest in music continued throughout his life and upon his retirement he became organist and choirmaster at St Margaret's Church, Alderton (1983–85). After leaving Oxford he was appointed Lecturer in Zoology at Nottingham University College (1932) and was progressively Head of the Zoology Department (1934–49) and Professor of Zoology (1949–74). He was deputy Vice-Chancellor of the University in 1956–59. His time at Nottingham University was broken by periods in North America as Rockefeller Foundation Fellow in Comparative Physiology at McGill (1939) and Harvard (1940) and, later, in South

America as Visiting Professor at the University of Buenos Aires (1970) and Sao Paulo (1972). His scientific interests were in endocrinology and he established a strong research laboratory in this subject at Nottingham and published several text-books in endocrinology, and the zoology of the lower chordates. He acted as European editor of the *Journal of General and Comparative Endocrinology* (1960–74) and was the series editor of a number of endocrinological and zoological monographs. He was elected Fellow of the Royal Society in 1967 and in 1971–72 was a Vice-President. In 1976 he was awarded the Frink Medal of the London Zoological Society. One of his students, Alan Matty (later Professor at Aston and Stirling), remembered him as a 'brilliant lecturer and outstanding committee man'. It is fitting that it should have fallen to him to host the reception at the Natural History Museum in 1980 which climaxed the Charter celebrations.

John Postgate (President 1982–83) was the 16th President of the Institute. His career started with a first-class degree in chemistry at Balliol College, Oxford, in 1946. He then developed his interest in bacterial biochemistry first at Oxford and then, successively, at the Teddington Chemical Research Laboratory and at Porton Down Microbiological Research Establishment. In 1962–63 he was Visiting Professor at the University of Illinois and, later, in 1977–78 he returned to the USA as Visiting Professor at the University of Oregon. In 1963 he was appointed Assistant Director of ARC Unit of Nitrogen Fixation and two years later he took up the chair of microbiology at the University of Sussex. In 1977 he was elected FRS. In 1965 Postgate was one of the first group of MIBiols to be elected Fellows of the Institute. Like Ernest Barrington before him, Postgate was a musician and deeply interested in music — in his case, however, it was jazz rather than organ music. In 1973 he published *A Plain Man's Guide to Jazz* and entertained the Institute's members at a Guildford AGM with a spirited performance on the saxophone. He wrote a regular column for *Jazz Monthly* and published many reviews of jazz recordings. His many scientific publications centred on nitrogen fixation and he contributed a text entitled *Nitrogen fixation* in 1967 to the Institute's *Studies in Biology* series.

J L Harley (President 1984–85) gained first-class honours in botany at Oxford and went on to gain a DPhil researching the mycorrhiza of beech trees. When war was declared in 1939, Jack Harley enlisted in the Royal Corps of Signals and had achieved the rank of Lieutenant-Colonel by the time he was demobbed in 1945. After another spell at Oxford he was appointed Professor of Botany at Sheffield in 1965 and later returned to Oxford as Professor of Forest Science. He was involved in many scientific organisations and societies, including the Agricultural Research Council and the Rothamsted Experimental Station, and was President of the British Mycological Society (1967–68), British Ecological Society (1970–72) and Section K of the British Association (1972), and was awarded the Gold Medal of the Linnean Society (1968). In recognition of his many contributions he was appointed CBE in 1979.

Sir Kenneth Blaxter (President 1986–87) gained first-class honours in agriculture at Reading University in 1939. He saw war service in the Royal Artillery and returned to an appointment at the Ministry of Agriculture's Veterinary Research Laboratory at Weybridge, followed by a year as Commonwealth Fund Fellow at the University of Illinois. On his return to Britain he was appointed Head of Nutrition at the Hannah Research Institute at Ayr. In 1965 he became Director of the Rowett Research Institute in Aberdeen, where he remained until his retirement in 1982. Sir Kenneth made many fundamental contributions to the scientific understanding of the nutritional needs and energy metabolism of ruminant livestock. The importance of these contributions was recognised by Fellowship of the Royal Society of Edinburgh (he served as President 1979–82), Fellowship of the Royal Society, Fellowship of numerous overseas scientific academies, and honorary doctorates from four universities. He also played a part in forming Government policy as chairman of the Cabinet Office merit promotion panel and member of the advisory committee on releases to the environment. For these many contributions, scientific and advisory, Kenneth Blaxter was knighted in 1977.

Ronald Keay (President 1988–89) graduated in botany from Oxford in 1942 and almost immediately embarked for Nigeria, where he was destined to stay for 20 years, becoming Principal of the Forest School in Ibadan. On returning to England in 1962 he took up an appointment as Deputy Executive Secretary with the Royal Society and was deeply involved in its move from Burlington House to Carlton House Terrace in 1967 and, 10 years later, in 1977, he was appointed Executive Secretary. His many publications concentrated on West African botany, especially forestry, and reflect his early experience in Nigeria. After retirement from the Royal Society in 1985 Ronald Keay involved himself in many voluntary activities, amongst which were Vice-Chairman of the Ridley Committee of the Royal Horticultural Society (RHS), Chairman of the RHS library review committee, Treasurer of the Linnean Society, and Visiting Professor at the University of Essex.

Acknowledgements

My thanks in particular to Harry Grenville for much help and for allowing me to consult his archive and to Philip O'Donoghue for private communication, to the authors of the Minutes of Officers and Council Meetings at the Institute, and to contributors to *Biologist* throughout the 1980s, especially the sections on Institute affairs.

References

Anon (1980) The Institute's Divisions. *Biologist*, **27,** 151 – 152.

Anon (1981) Charter celebrations. *Biologist*, **28,** 98.

Beardmore J and Copp D (1981) UGC proposals for biology. *Biologist*, **28,** 182 – 183.

Wylson P (1983) 20 Queensberry Place, London SW7. *Biologist*, **30,** 135 – 137.

A ROYAL SOCIETY OF BIOLOGY?

Sam Berry CBiol FIBiol
Professor, Department of Biology, University College London,
and Former President, Linnean Society of London

❝ I was President of the Linnean Society for 1982–85. I chose as my first presidential address to review the relationship between the science of biology and its structures (Berry, 1983). I asked if the division of British biology into more than a hundred individual societies might be reducing the impact (and funding) of biology in relation to other sciences.

The Linnean is the oldest biological society in the world. It has two Royal Charters (1802, 1904), identifying the Society's object as 'the Cultivation of the Science of Natural History in all its branches', and retains great prestige. But for practising biologists it had become generally regarded as little more than a society concerned with taxonomy, particularly of plants. Its history has been one of repeated schism: in 1826 the Zoological Society of London split away from its parent, followed seven years later by the (Royal) Entomological Society. Perhaps the crowning indignity was the setting up in 1937 of the Systematics Association, sparked by frustration with the inertia and vested interests within the Linnean Society itself.

I had been impressed by a paper on *Learned Societies in 2031?* by Ronald Keay (at the time Executive Secretary of the Royal Society and subsequently President of the Institute), in which he talked about the 'coming together' of professional institutions and learned societies. In my presidential address, I expressed the personal hope for a 'growing together of societies ... to involve the Institute of Biology and lead eventually to a prestigious Royal Society of Biology'. Such a body could apply its resources to the benefit of its members without wasteful overlap, and would provide a way of relating to ABRC, Government, statutory bodies and other non-governmental organisations in a way that did not (and still does not) exist.

Building on a previous — rejected — suggestion by Lord Zuckermann, I discussed with the Secretary of the Zoological Society of London (ZSL) the possibility of developing closer links. This led to an invitation being sent out in the names of Arthur Bell, then the Director of the Royal Botanic Gardens; Bill Chaloner, my successor as Linnean President; Dick Laws, the Secretary of the ZSL, and myself to a group of senior biologists. We invited them to a meeting on 29 April 1985 to consider the establishment of a central forum or focus for British biology. We agreed that there were grounds for continuing the discussion in a wider forum; this took place on 29 October that year under the auspices of the Biological Council, as the umbrella organisation for biological societies.

I reported on the background in *Biologist* (Berry, 1985). Ron Hedley, Director of the Natural History Museum, was enthusiastic about a biological grouping and Eric Denton, Director of the Marine Biological Association, was supportive. Jack Harley, President of the Institute of Biology, who had been invited to the 29 April meeting but had not attended, was against the proposal for a 'Royal Society of Biology' as he felt it would be an attack on the autonomy and effectiveness of the Institute. In the event, most of the time of the 29 October meeting was spent discussing the possibility of a single research council for the whole of biology. No progress was made on the main theme.

Meanwhile, I talked with Lord Dainton, who had been involved in the highly successful federation of two leading learned societies with the Royal Institute of Chemistry into a Royal Society of Chemistry. He suggested I solicit the help of the university professors of biology. There was at the time no effective grouping of botanical professors, but the zoologists were very supportive, and for some years we had an active Zoology Liaison Group between the ZSL and the professorial meeting (Berry, 1988). This lasted until the ZSL became bound up with its own problems and the meeting evolved into one of the Heads of University Biology Departments.

The Royal Society of Biology idea is now on the back burner. The Institute of Biology is more influential than it was in the mid-1980s, and is working with the many individual biological societies. However, I still believe that a Royal Society of Biology will eventually emerge and will be for the benefit of British biology. Its time will come as we face increasing threats from industry, bureaucrats and even from society itself: I hope that time will not be too long hence. **99**

References

Berry R J (1983) The evolution of British biology, *Biological Journal of the Linnean Society*, **20**, 327 – 352.

Berry R J (1985) Is divided biology weakened biology?, *Biologist*, **32**, 211 – 212.

Berry R J (1988) Heads of University Biology Departments, *Biologist*, **35**, 257.

A MILLENNIUM ENDS

Wilson Wall PhD EurBiol CBiol MIBiol
International consultant in genetics, whose latest popular book is
Sexing the Parrot, Changing the World with DNA

With the dawning of 1990 and the start of the fifth decade of the Institute of Biology, great changes were taking place in both the science of biology and the Institute itself. Matters were set in train in 1990 when the United Kingdom became the first country to sanction the use of a genetically modified organism in food, a yeast that had an enhanced ability to take up and use malt sugars. By 1996 0.75 per cent of maize grown in the USA was genetically modified, but by 1999 this had increased to 39 per cent. From March 1999 all genetically modified food has had to be labelled as such in the United Kingdom. All this has kept the Institute of Biology in a premier position as an advisory group to both Government and the public on matters of biological science.

The fifth decade of the Institute of Biology saw the election of Peter Biggs as President in 1990, with the membership standing at 15 224. This figure was less than the previous year. Indeed, the membership had been declining since the early 1980s, and would continue to do so until the mid-1990s. It was said by many members that this reduction in membership was a direct result of two factors, most notably that subscriptions had been increasing at a rate not matched by public sector salaries: in 1990 the subscription for Members was £41 and Fellows £58; by 1999 this had risen to £70 for Members and £97 for Fellows. This was significant with respect to the other reason for a declining membership: many biologists were starting to perceive the Institute as a self-reverential club of little tangible benefit to the member. Indeed, for most members of the Institute the only contact they had was *Biologist* which, in 1999, was available as a subscription for only £31 — expensive, but a lot less than the membership fee. The line of thinking that the Institute of Biology was doing little except send out *Biologist* was unfortunate, because this was not all that it was doing, but the problem was that the other important work tended to be hidden from the membership.

Absorbing the Biological Council

Possibly the biggest move forward in 1990 was, in the words of the General Secretary of the Institute, 'a significant date in the history of the Institute of Biology'. This date was Monday 24 September 1990, when the Biological Council voted to amalgamate with the Institute, which had voted in favour of the plan earlier in the year. Surprisingly little had been heard of the Biological Council for many years, even though it predated the Institute and, as we have seen, it had been set up as a forum for learned societies to discuss areas of common interest between them.

Professor P Biggs, President of the Institute, welcoming Prof R S K Wood, President of the Biological Council, as the Council joined the Institute in 1990.

It was, therefore, a very important umbrella organisation for biologists everywhere (a list appears in the Appendix). The completed amalgamation of the Biological Council and the Institute of Biology was celebrated on 6 November 1991 at a dinner held at the Royal College of Physicians, with over 100 guests representing the two bodies.

EurBiol

That same year, 1990, saw further steps in the process that would culminate in June 1995 with the announcement that Institute members could apply to become European Biologists, although it was in 1993 that the European Communities Biologists' Association (ECBA) agreed in principle to the title EurBiol. This was introduced because it was perceived, correctly, that with the single European market biologists would become more mobile professionally than ever before. This would mean that it would be necessary to unify the standards of biological qualifications, or have a unified professional qualification. Since standardisation of educational levels would be impossible, given that all the countries of the European Union have different ways of describing their national qualifications, it was seen as necessary for each participating country to have a body that could oversee and control standards for professional biologists.

Academic biologists have always moved freely around the world, but in the case of biologists who are more industry-based, especially those who do consultancy work, it was always difficult for the employers to know for certain what the level of the consult-

Dr R Priestley, General Secretary of the Institute, raising a toast to the EurBiol at its inauguration in 1995.

ant really was — until the arrival of EurBiol. Indeed, it was not only biologists that had the potential for this trans-European qualification, for there are now such diverse groups as EurChem, EurGeo and EurEng, for chemists, geologists and engineers respectively. The new qualification finally arrived in 1995, although it had originally been mooted in the 1980s and was given added impetus in 1992, when the General Secretary of the Institute, Robert Priestley, became Chairman of the ECBA. The problem of the professional status of consultants was partly addressed by the production of the Institute's *Directory of Consultants in Biology*. The problem with this, like so many directories of consultants, is getting the directory to the people who need to see it. There is, after all, no point in a directory that no one uses.

Problems loom

The Institute of Biology had been developing in the background into a considerable force for professional biologists under the presidency of Biggs. He recalls that his first impression in becoming President was that the Institute lacked an overall structure. He soon found that membership was still going down — indeed, in 1991 expenditure of the Institute was £30 400 greater than income. Overexpenditure had occurred the previous year, as well as on other occasions in the past. Although this would be a serious problem if it happened every year, generally income equalled expenditure, so overall the long-term picture was not so bad as it seemed at first glance. At least the Institute remained financially solvent. However, at the time, while it was perceived as necessary for the Institute of Biology to widen its horizons, financial constraints meant that there had to be cutbacks in activities, rather than expansions. One target for extra economies was always the Branches. The Branch Secretaries were becoming increasingly vocal, and began to find a sense of common purpose in resisting such proposals. Biggs realised that the Branches had little input into decisions at headquarters, and he set about formalising the presence of a Branch Representative at executive meetings.

During 1991 a major step forward for the Institute was extending the space available at headquarters, which was becoming cramped through the increasing demands of the affiliated societies. But there was another factor, the thought that the Institute of Biology might require space to set up a 'Centre for Biology'. So when the Wellcome Trust decided to refurbish a building on the Euston Road in London and move out of its property in Regent's Park, the possibility was raised that the Institute of Biology might purchase the vacant building. This would have meant leaving Queensberry Place completely. It was soon discovered that this property was beyond the budget of the Institute, but around this time the building next door, 22 Queensberry Place, came up for sale, having until then been a secretarial college. The purchase was completed in 1992 for £915 000. This large sum of money had to be raised in part by a mortgage. Upon taking over number 22 it was realised that the expense had not stopped, as considerable building work was required, not just to make the property suitable for Institute staff but also to comply with current fire regulations.

The high cost of the property and necessary alterations resulted in part of the building being let to the Kensington International School. This was, and for many remains, a controversial act. This is because the school caters primarily for under-12s. Nothing was wrong with that, but as the children initially shared the entrance of 20 Queensberry

Mr A C Mohan MBE HonMIBiol, Head of Management Services of the Institute and staff member for 29 years.

Place with the Institute, it was perceived by many to compromise the status of the Institute of Biology as a learned society. Even when, much later, the school used the entrance to number 22, there was still the question of whether the Institute should have junior school artwork stuck to the windows for passers-by to puzzle over and wonder about the intellectual capacity of biologists within. There was also, in the early years of the let, the question of security. The school starts early, and it had been noted that when it opened for business it was possible simply to walk from the school into the Institute of Biology offices.

The central position of Institute headquarters meant that hiring the committee room to other organisations provided a steadily increasing income, and by 1995 the Honorary Treasurer, Alan Cadogan, reported that £53 600 had been raised in rental charges. In light of the sterling work that A C Mohan, Head of Management Services, had undertaken during his 28-year of tenure with the Institute, and especially his work in originally securing 20 Queensberry Place, he was awarded the distinction of Honorary MIBiol.

A new structure

Along with this change in the accommodation of the Institute, there was now a growing perception that it would be necessary to review its management structure. This was especially true in the light of all the affiliated societies that were gathering under the Institute's umbrella. To complete this transition an extraordinary general meeting was held immediately after the annual general meeting in April. This EGM was to ratify the amalgamation of the Biological Council, subject to the approval of the Biological Council, the Privy Council and the Charity Commissioners. The vote of Members and Fellows present was unanimous, with 58 votes in favour, none against and no abstentions. With this change, by the end of the year the individual learned societies affiliated to the Biological Council were invited to affiliate directly to the Institute of Biology.

Meanwhile there were changes in the chairing of the history committee. The present incumbent, Brian Ford, who had been a founder member of the original Group (as is this author), was elected in 1990. Our meetings included conferences held at locations associated with the historical figures under discussion: Berkeley, Gloucestershire (Edward Jenner); Selborne, Hampshire (Gilbert White); Down House, Kent (Charles Darwin); and Braintree, Essex (John Ray). Some of these meetings were held in conjunction with other societies interested in the individuals or their science: the John Ray Trust at Braintree, the Jenner Educational Trust at Berkeley, the Charles Darwin Museum in the original house at Downe, etc. We have welcomed distinguished guests (including Desmond King-Hele and Stephen Jay Gould) and speakers from mainland Europe and the United States. Members of the committee met in various locations, including Boston, Massachusetts, where several members were speaking. The committee continued to expand its publication, *Biology History*, which ran to 18 issues over eight years and contained reports of meetings and symposia, book reviews, and original articles. Although its print run approached 1000, it proved to be difficult to co-ordinate with the Institute's activities and publication has since been suspended.

Among the committee's activities was the compiling of this book, and one of our members, Bernard Thomason, has been appointed Honorary Archivist to the Institute. We can thus ensure that Institute activities are properly recorded in the future. As this book goes to press we are planning a meeting to mark the exact centenary of genetics in Britain. The term was coined at a meeting in London on 8 May 1900, and it is on 8 May 2000 that Mike Buttolph is organising a half-day symposium to commemorate the event (and to mark the Institute's half-century). After much negotiation with the current committee Chairman, the Group metamorphosed first into a Sector and, latterly, into a Network, which perhaps indicates the increasing significance of the Internet in academic work.

The Institute also began to look to the historical dimension with the granting of a coat of arms for the Institute of Biology, which appeared for the first time on the cover of *Biologist* in November 1991, and has continued to appear in smaller form on the cover ever since. The right to apply for a coat of arms from the College of Arms was part of the Royal Charter that had been given in 1979. The original proposal to gain a coat of arms was announced in 1990 and was quickly followed by establishment of a working party to produce a draft design for submission to the College of Arms. There were several attempts to produce an image that was not

The grant of arms for the Institute, which appeared for the first time on the cover of Biologist *in November 1991.*

only commensurate with the dignity of the Institute but, also, which would never look dated and would be acceptable to the College of Arms. Finally the Council of the Institute decided upon a design that was submitted to the College of Arms.

Slight changes were made to the original design, but it retained all its essentials. Once ratified it was given an official blazon (the written description that should allow reproduction of the image), but this is probably only useful to those familiar with the terminology. Perhaps many biologists familiar with taxonomic nomenclature will be able to work out the colours and structure from the text. The blazon is reproduced in full:

> **Arms:** *Per bend Azure and Vert in sinister chief an Eagle displayed Or beaked and legged Gules and in dexter base a Cinquefoil also Or pierced and charged with five Ermine spots radiating outwards Sable a Sun in splendour issuant in dexter canton with one straight ray extending to sinister base Gold.*
>
> **Crest:** *Upon a helm with a Wreath Or and Gules an Elm Tree proper issuant from a Coronet its finials in the form of Garbs and the rim Or embellished palewise with a Double Helix Gules and Sable.*
>
> **Mantled:** *Azure doubled Or to the dexter and Vert doubled Or to the sinister.*
>
> **Supporters:** *On the dexter a Galapagos Marine Iguana and on the sinister an Otter the Compartment comprising an Island of pebbles all proper amid Water barry wavy Azure and Argent.*
>
> **Motto:** *Scientiam vitae propagare.*

The reason for all the various bits and pieces on the coat of arms can be more easily explained than followed through the above description which, although exactly correct, will seem impenetrable to many readers. The shield has three symbols which are redolent of the pivotal nature of energy transfer in biological systems. There is the sun, transferring energy into our world (although we now know that primary energy does not come only from the sun, as chemical energy from deep-sea vents also adds energy to our biosphere). A ray of sun splits the shield diagonally between a blue sky background with an eagle on it and a green background with a flower upon it, which represents the importance of photosynthesis and the transfer of energy through a food chain to a top carnivore (in this case the eagle). The flower has five petals, each one representing one of the five kingdoms of life: Prokaryotae, Protoctista, Fungi, Plantae and Animalia.

Above the shield is a helmet with a closed visor, the traditional manner of indicating a corporate body, like the Institute of Biology, in heraldry. Above the helmet is a crest comprising a crown and a tree, joined to the helmet by a wreath of red and gold twisted ribbons, the red symbolising that most important molecule, haemoglobin. The rim of the crown has a red and black double helix, symbolising DNA. Associated with this is the circlet of the crown, made up of sheaves of wheat, reminding us of the importance of biology in the selective breeding of our food organisms to feed the world. Rising from the centre of the crown, above everything else, is an elm tree, serving a triple purpose as the tree of life, the tree of knowledge, and a reminder of the need to be vigilant with respect to man's accidental, or deliberate, introduction of alien disease organisms.

On either side of the shield there are supporters, an otter and an iguana, emerging from water symbolising evolution. Specifically the otter signifies the need for conservation, and the iguana the voyage of the *Beagle* with Charles Darwin to the Galapagos islands.

Finally there is the motto, *Scientiam vitae propagare*, which translates as *To propagate the knowledge of life*. The arms began to appear on the front cover of *Biologist*, though other innovations were taking place here too.

A new *Biologist*

The Institute's journal had undergone major changes in previous years, but was now to undergo even greater change. The two most significant changes that had taken place earlier were the move to a larger A4 format in 1990, and the simultaneous introduction of colour on the cover, although the contents remained steadfastly in black and white. These changes took place under excellent stewardship.

What changed in 1992 was the manner in which these two journals were run. Helen Johnson had been working as editor of *Biologist* and the *Journal of Biological Education* on what was essentially a freelance basis. It had been realised that, since the major contact for most members was *Biologist*, this should be encouraged to develop.

A range of recent covers of Biologist.

The change came in the form of appointment of full-time editors of both the *Journal of Biological Education* and *Biologist*. Clare Chatham was appointed Executive Editor of the *Journal of Biological Education* and Susan Silver Editor of *Biologist*. These were both staff positions, so the part-time nature of the position of editor was finally ended. Chatham was previously employed in various publication houses and was registered with the Open University for an art degree. Silver initially came from a scientific background, as a graduate in zoology of Bedford College, London, with a PhD from Queen Mary College, London. Like many scientists she moved into publishing, starting with *Nature* and then Academic Press before becoming Assistant Editor of the *British Dental Journal* and Editor of *Biologist*.

During Silver's editorship many changes were made to *Biologist*, not least with the introduction of colour illustrations in the September 1992 edition, although it would be February 1998 before it became full-colour throughout. It was this time also when *Biobits* appeared as a newsletter separate from *Biologist* rather than being an integral part of the journal. It had been said that when *Biologist* was more or less run by com-mittee, that is before there was a full-time editor, there was a tendency to publish 'any old rubbish'. With the increasing status of *Biologist* and its being abstracted, this situation changed. While it is still, for historical reasons, published five times a year, it would not be difficult to fill at least six issues annually (from 2001, *Biologist* will be published six times a year). While unsolicited manuscripts are welcome, most of the articles are commissioned. A few subscriptions have been taken out for *Biologist*, but this is not seen as an important part of the revenue for its production. What is seen as important is the advertising revenue, which covers approximately 20 per cent of the costs. With the separate publication of *Biobits*, the November 1999 issue had grown by eight additional pages.

Many of these changes are a result of a report commissioned by the Institute into how the publication was produced. The committee making the report was chaired by Bernard Dixon. Broadly, it was recommended that the Institute should produce new journals and increase *Biologist* from five to 10 issues a year. Ten issues were suggested because it is normal for this sort of journal to regard August and December as 'dead' months for publishing. This increase would require the creation of five new editorial posts. As it can be imagined, the huge increase in costs would have put a very great financial burden on the Institute and so most recommendations were not implemented.

Time for change

The now-accepted dictum of 'equal opportunities' has found favour with the Institute but has not, unfortunately, been interpreted into fact. There has been a regrettable lack of women on the various committees of the Institute. Precisely why this should be so is unknown, but we hope it will be rectified. It is also reflected in the make-up of the Fellows of the Institute, of whom less than one per cent are female. Considering the large numbers of women employed in biology this is a pity; besides which, the majority of students taking biology at university are now women and they should clearly be represented in larger numbers within the Institute.

At the end of 1992 a change took place in the structure of the Institute of Biology. This was undertaken for three main reasons:

- To improve liaison between the various parts of the Institute.
- To integrate the activities of the Biological Council, which by this time no longer existed as a separate entity.
- To enable the affiliated societies to play a role in the development of the Institute.

During this period Council was reduced from a rather unwieldy 46 members to a still rather large, but more manageable, 21 by the end of the century. This rearrangement of the Institute resulted in six main changes, namely:

Although there may be disproportionately few women of the Institute, some staff members were found to model the Institute's sweatshirts in 1998 – Tracey Gerrard (left), PA to the Head of Membership and Fiona Wilson, Head of Membership.

- A new executive committee, which would be responsible for liaison between Council and the various committees.
- A simplification of the committee structure, so that committees would be grouped together into 'activities'.
- Provision for the formation of a committee designated Animal Welfare in Research and Education, given the misleading acronym AWARE (presumably to distinguish it from the Atomic Weapons Research Establishment, AWRE).
- Changes to the way in which committee members are appointed; it now became possible for members to nominate individuals.
- Societies affiliated to the Institute could serve as 'observers' on various committees.
- Every society affiliated to the Institute would have the right of a representative on the Affiliated Societies Forum.

By this time the President was Sir Colin Spedding, who is well known among Institute members as a collector of proverbs. This is not merely an accidental hobby, but one that seems to have arisen in order to inject some humour into lectures. During Spedding's presidency it was recognised that financial constraints meant that

The first four Presidents of the Institute of the 1990s: (clockwise from top left) Peter Biggs, Sir Colin Spedding, F A Hibbert, Brian Heap.

cutbacks, rather than the more desirable expansion, of Institute activities would continue. However, during 1992 the refurbishment of 20–22 Queensberry Place was completed and the Centre for Biology was established. Although rather grandly titled, the Centre for Biology was in fact an address which other biological societies could use for administration, organising meetings, collection of subscriptions and other secretarial activities.

During 1993 implementation of the recommendations of the committee under Biggs were made. These broadly altered the structure of the various Institute committees and established a public policy committee. This was in recognition of the fact that, whatever else the Institute did, it simply could not be left out of consultations where matters of biology were important in framing Government policy. Changes were also made to the application procedure for Fellowship of the Institute of Biology. It had long been recognised that the old system did not necessarily always work because it was incumbent on the nominators of an individual for Fellowship to make out a good case for why a person should be elected. The new system put the emphasis on the candidates stating why they were eligible, so they could make out the best case for themselves.

A good example of the increasingly proactive activities of the Institute of Biology came with the publication of the Food Safety Policy Group, *Policy Studies no. 5,* on the safety and social acceptance of genetically engineered food. This was quickly followed by a response to the Department of Environment consultation paper on river quality. This may not seem at first to be so directly associated with the Institute of Biology, but of course it is. Flora and fauna in water accurately reflect the health of a body of water, and a competent biologist can quickly and easily determine the source of a polluting incident from the plants, animals and microorganisms found above and below the source of the problem.

Besides these positive events there was a negative one at the Institute. The premises at 20–22 Queensberry Place had to be provided with extensive security simply because, for no apparent reason, 'some unknown hooligans' had twice broken windows in the building during the night and caused considerable internal damage by throwing red paint. It was speculated that the culprits might have been protesting about the use of animals in experiments in biological laboratories.

A considerable effort was made during this year of 1994, as every year, to increase membership of the Institute. This was at least in part because it was recognised that even though membership was going down, new members could be recruited from the student population at a much reduced subscription. It was hoped in this way to change the original perception of the membership base as being mostly teachers. This perception was, indeed, slowly changing, but numbers were still slipping.

This was destined to be the low point of our numbers with only 14 500 members. Since 1994 numbers slowly increased and they have done so ever since, until at the beginning of the 21st century we have a membership of 16 362 — the highest in our 50-year history. Whether the start of this change had anything to do with the

Discount '94 campaign is unclear — not only did membership go up, but that was the first year that Institute's income exceeded £1 million. The Discount '94 campaign for members took the form of getting current members to canvas their colleagues to join the Institute. During 1994, if a member of the Institute recruited another full member, the Institute would send the recruiter a cheque for 50 per cent of the new member's subscription. Whether this imaginative piece of marketing worked, or how many new recruits it generated, is unknown, but the Institute was very definitely on a rising tide of membership from 1994 onwards. This campaign was not merely an attempt by the Institute to become ever more wealthy, although this was a consideration, as it is for any society, but as much as anything it was motivated by a desire for the Institute to become a far more influential force in the development of Government policy and the informed understanding of the public in the increasingly complicated and important area of modern biology.

Enter the Olympiad

During 1994 there was a further recognition by the international community of the value of the Institute, in the form of an invitation to join the International Biology Olympiad. The physicists and chemists had already been involved in this sort of thing for some time, so it was the lagging child of biology that brought up the rear. In the spring of 1995 a committee was established under the chairmanship of Norma Broadbridge with Sir Walter Bodmer as President. By the autumn of that year a 'pilot' Olympiad had been arranged. The format which was introduced that year is still generally followed. The process starts in the autumn and the competition is

The British Biology Olympiad winners for 1998 outside Buckingham Palace with Norma Broadbridge (left) and Andy Headford (right). The new competition for students has been a very successful initiative of the Institute, pioneered by Norma Broadbridge.

resolved in the spring and summer of the following year. By 1998 it was finally possible to organise and send a team to the International Biology Olympiad. This first team was not only invited to a garden party with Her Majesty the Queen, but then went on to score a gold, two silvers and a bronze — the highest-ever score for a first-time entry.

Informing the outside world

The year 1994 also saw the reintroduction of the *Directory of Consultants*. This had appeared sporadically during the 1960s and 1970s, with the last edition, the seventh, appearing in 1981. While this has been seen as valuable for consultants who work with biologists, there is no doubt that for consultants working with people or companies that do not have any Institute of Biology contact, such as insurance companies or lawyers, the promotion of this directory has not been a success. For a consultant, the only way of reaching these non-biological potential customers is to appear in their own professional directories, rather than the Institute of Biology directory.

One of the changes of direction that the Institute of Biology undertook in 1994 may not have been recognised at the time for the important event that it was: to disseminate knowledge to the public. This was a response to the growing public awareness of the power and importance of biology within society. With the development of an actively informed citizenship, the public debate of areas central to biology gradually developed away from such things as medical ethics — a traditional area of debate — into areas like food safety and the environmental issues of conservation and pollution. Another area of growing public concern, and one with which the Institute of Biology was directly involved, was biodiversity: what it means and what would happen to us all if we lost even a small part of this diversity. Increasing interest among the public on this subject stimulated many different whole-organism projects, just to get to a position where there was some idea of just how many species there are extant on this planet.

In 1995 the annual general meeting of the Institute of Biology was held in Edinburgh. This was a particularly suitable choice for a site outside London because under the presidency of Alan Hibbert, who had been elected the previous year, it matched up as an integral part of Biology '95 and the Edinburgh International Science Festival. Instead of a simple afternoon AGM, as had been usual in the past, the AGM was embedded in the second day of the three-day meeting. It was during 1995 that the first EurBiol qualifications were conferred. There were 76 applications from six member states, of which 27 were from the UK, including the present author.

Rise and fall of the MRes

It was during 1995 that the Government compromised on one aspect of its plans that had been heralded as a great move forward in tertiary education, the Master of Research degree, MRes. The idea of this new qualification was greeted with a certain disdain by all the major professional learned societies, including the Institute of Biology, the Royal Society of Chemistry and the Institute of Physics. Even worse, the Government proposal was a depressing proposition for potential PhD students. It should be remembered that a PhD is not a goal in itself, but a training degree for research scientists. The proposal to extend the period by an additional year with a mandatory MRes, a year-long postgraduate degree of Master of Research — before being allowed to take up a PhD — was a cause of some concern. Such was the feeling among the various societies and, it should be added, the scientists themselves who would have ended up as underpaid for yet another year, that the Government eventually changed its mind. There are still MRes degrees, but they are seen in a different light from that originally perceived by the Government.

Celebrations

It may seem strange, in some ways, that the Institute of Biology is only just celebrating its 50th year, since so many of the other learned scientific societies are much older. For example, the Institute of Physics is 126 years old in the year 2000 and the Chemical Society started life in 1841, changing its name to the Royal Society of Chemistry in 1980. Admittedly, biology has only come of age in the last 100 years, but even so, specialised biological societies have been around for longer than the Institute of Biology. An example here is the Society for General Microbiology, which was founded in 1945 and celebrated a Golden Jubilee in 1995, while the British Ecological Society was founded in 1913 and the Genetical Society in 1919. Many natural history societies date back over the centuries. The essential difference between biology and physics or chemistry is simply one of range and specialisation. While chemistry and physics have a unified theme running through all their activities, biological disciplines are connected only by that most nebulous of concepts — life.

During 1995 the Institute of Biology recognised two exceptional scientists by awarding them Honorary Fellowship of the Institute. These were James Watson and Francis Crick, who had carried out their work on the structure of DNA at the Cavendish Laboratory, Cambridge, where a group of chemists and physicists were looking at the three-dimensional structure of biological molecules. Since it is rare for biologists to contribute in such a significant way to basic physical sciences, it a testament to the diversity and encompassing nature of biology that the progress of the science is not confined to people who would describe themselves as biologists. This also reflects the blurred boundaries of the science, with crossover points in areas as diverse as biochemistry, biophysics and bioinfomatics.

During the first half of the 1990s the Institute had been running its membership list on what was becoming an increasingly out-of-date computer system. The membership list reflected the paucity of information that the Institute had about the members, itself a reflection of the limitations of the computer system. As a consequence a new computer system was purchased in 1995 at a cost of £55 000, and at the beginning of 1996 a new questionnaire was sent out to all members in the hope that they would respond and thereby increase the information that the Institute held, so that a better and more responsive Institute of Biology would emerge. Broadly speaking, the questions covered work, qualifications, areas of expertise and interests and personal details, in order to gain a general idea of the requirements and structure of the membership. Acknowledging that there is always a reluctance to fill in a questionnaire, the Institute organised a reply-paid envelope and a prize draw of £100 — it seems to have worked.

The task force

Our President, Brian Heap, launched a task force in 1996. Its main activity turned out to be producing a new plan that would take the Institute up to the year 2000. In this same year of 1996 two surveys were carried out, the first of members of the Institute of Biology, and the second of a survey of non-members. The members' survey, of 1500 targeted individuals, resulted in 402 responses, which although a small proportion of the total membership did provide an insight into the attitudes of members. The most interesting thing about this survey was that it was plain that those who responded thought *Biologist* was an important way of keeping in touch with biology as a whole and that Chartered Biologist was an important title for professional status. There were other findings, such as a high value given to the Institute's responses to Government on policy issues, representation on educational bodies, and development of biological curriculum.

Perhaps the more interesting of these two surveys was the one which dealt with non-members of the Institute of Biology. This was an inspired use of resources since it gave an insight not into why people joined the Institute, but why they did not. A total of 1350 questionnaires were distributed to non-member biologists across a wide range of employment sectors. Of these 415 replies were received, of which 93 per cent had heard of the Institute of Biology, although this may simply be that only those who knew of the Institute replied. Most of the respondents voiced similar opinions to the members' survey, with networking and keeping in touch with other biologists being far more important to non-members. The Chartered Biologist title was seen as far less important by these non-members.

Influencing the outside world

In April 1996, the Institute was busy with the launch of its website at the Scientific Computing Exhibition, held in Telford, and the Institute's 47th AGM, held in London. Also in April the Institute of Biology National Conference involved a group of eminent scientists trying their hand at an always risky game: soothsaying. Their brief was to consider biosciences and society in the 21st century. Some thought it impossible to guess what might develop; after all, at the end of the 19th century nobody could have guessed the leap forward that genetics would make 50 years later. The general trend of thought seems to have been rather negative, lifted by the possibility of solutions to human-devised environmental disasters, overcrowding of the planet, or preventing the production of a genetic underclass. There were notable exceptions, however, with Lewis Wolpert taking an upbeat view of the use of scientific developments, rather than concentrating on the problems that we are likely to face in the next century.

It was during 1996 that the Institute of Biology decided to raise its profile and become the voice of British biology. This included a strategy plan for the Institute, which was drawn up by Heap's task force. Underpinning this complicated activity was a members' questionnaire, discussions with chairs of committees, chairs of Branches and last, but by no means least, representatives of the approximately 75 affiliated societies. The final document ran to 35 pages, and like all such management documents it was not always written in such a way as to be 'understood by someone who spends most of their time in wellington boots looking for invertebrates'. Although this could be seen as a negative attitude, it could also be seen as something rather more positive (this respondent was not wearing wellingtons at the time) and proves that at least some of the membership was quite happy to let a task force lead the Institute into the next century.

The 'mission statement' made it quite clear that the primary aim of the Institute of Biology, as stated in the original Charter, 'to advance the science and practice of biology, to advance education therein and to co-ordinate and encourage the study of biology and its application', would not be tampered with. These are, after all, high ideals and in their own right laudable. Within this framework there were five main areas of activity that the Institute wanted to develop via the strategic plan. These were:
- Promoting biology and the biological sciences.
- Fostering the public understanding of the life sciences generally.
- Serving the needs of members.
- Enhancing the status of the biology profession as a whole.
- Representing members and the profession of biology to Government and other bodies that influence biology.

To put these aims into practice it was seen as necessary radically to restructure the gradually altering Institute by major changes to the committees and boards, so that the Institute became more efficient and capable of implementing the changes. This was done by setting up five new boards, each of which was concerned with a specific area of Institute of Biology policy, and each of which was chaired by a member of the Institute executive committee. The five boards were:
- Professional affairs, chaired by Mike Elves.
- Science policy, chaired by Peter Shewry.

- Education and training, chaired by Sheila Turner.
- Public relations, chaired by Sir Colin Spedding.
- Management, chaired by Peter Bunyan.

As part of the strategic plan it was decided to 'bring the Branches further into the fold'. This was to be carried out by a National Co-ordinator of Branches who would make sure that the Branches were kept in touch with the executive committee and vice versa. The first Co-ordinator appointed was Eric Carter, who continued in this post until the end of 1999. One of the differences this made was that the new *Biobits* allowed far more space for describing the various branch meetings and outings that had taken place in the recent past.

A change of name?

One of the things that the task force came across, which would have made a difference to all the members, was that there was some interest in changing the name of the Institute. Several suggestions were made for the new name, such as Royal Institute of Biology, Institute of Biological Sciences, Institute of Biology and Biotechnology, Institute of Biosciences, or the Institute of Professional Biologists. To change to a Royal Institute of Biology would require permission from the offices of the Royal Family and the Privy Council, but any other name change would be a rather simpler process. When the members were presented with the two sides of the issue and asked their opinions, there was much debate but the overall feeling was that biology perfectly defined 'the study of life'. This encompassed biotechnology and molecular biology, so 'Institute of Biology' covers the entire, 'disparate' field of life. Most members felt that biology was subdivided enough, without the Institute that wants to be the voice of British biology becoming anything less than the natural home for all biologists.

While all these deliberations were going on the Institute was still producing responses on a wide range of subjects, such as Scotland's coasts, a proposal for a UK Academy of Medicine, and sustainable development. This is an important aspect of the Institute's activities because as a professional body, rather than a learned society, it has the resources to be involved in wide-ranging consultations about biology. This is an area in which a specialised learned society, unless very large, does not have the resources to participate. There are many other differences between a learned society and the Institute, which is why there is no conflict of interest between the Institute and the many affiliated societies.

Changes of direction

By 1997 the new computer system was in position at Queensberry Place and it was used to analyse the results of the 1996 membership survey with regards to the type of employment in which members were involved. What this showed was that the

swing away from the Institute was mostly by teachers, with a move towards a more varied employment base. So 26 per cent were involved in education at all levels, 12 per cent describing themselves as 'teachers' and 14 per cent as 'lecturers', while 24 per cent of respondents described their work as some form of research and development and 19 per cent as management. There is undoubtedly some cross-over between these tasks in many jobs, but it does give a general picture of the position of members.

Towards the end of 1997 it was realised that the appointment of a Chief Executive of the Institute of Biology would be necessary. It would radically change the position of the General Secretary, Priestley. This move was an inevitable result of the Institute changing direction and entering a new era, and Priestley therefore decided to leave the Institute after many years of work, 1989–97. The executive committee decided to make a temporary appointment of General Secretary while the whole situation was thought through, and Mike Fowler, Deputy Chairman of Plant Science International (PSI) plc, based in Cambridge, was appointed. This was only ever going to be a temporary solution and by June 1998, with John Norris in post as President of the Institute, Alan Malcolm — Director of the Institute of Food Research in Reading — was appointed as the Institute's first Chief Executive. Norris, who would take the Institute into the 21st century and its 50th anniversary, was also a non-executive Director of PSI and had recently retired from group research at Cadbury-Schweppes.

Strangely, in what was seen as an expanding area of science, the East Anglia Branch of the Institute folded for lack of support during 1998. It is hoped to resurrect this Branch at some later date. There has also been a change to the Charter by-laws. They now allow any person, who has reached the age of 16 and who can establish to the satisfaction of the Council that he or she is following an approved course of study leading to a biological qualification, to be admitted as a Student Member of the Institute. This is a timely idea for several reasons, not just to keep the membership rising, but also because those that go on to higher education in biology and a professional career would be likely to stay as members, changing their grade as appropriate.

During the early part of 1998 a major conference was planned under the title of *The quality of life*. Although there was an enthusiastic response from the membership and a number of high-profile speakers were on track to participate, it had to be cancelled. The commercial company that had been commissioned to organise this meeting had failed, with the resultant loss of the deposit paid by the Institute. Attempts to get a second company to take on the project were successful, but this too went under, so the project was dropped. Similarly the march of technology took a slight 'one step forward and one step back' with problems on the website. This was not a problem caused by the Institute, but a commercial problem with the Internet provider which rendered the site inaccessible for a time.

On the other hand, more than 15 000 copies of the new *Studies in Biology* were sold during 1998, these having been relaunched during the 1990s with Cambridge University Press. It was just as genetically modified foods became a hot topic with print and broadcast media that the Institute's new Chief Executive, Alan Malcolm, appeared on the scene. This was particularly fortunate as he was already well known in this field. As a result he made many appearances and interviews in order to clarify the situation for the general public. The President, Norris, also became involved proactively in this debate and the Institute produced a response to the Government request for information on this very subject.

The year 1999 saw the settling down of the new regime and the ever-growing impact of the Institute of Biology, not just as the voice of British biology but also as a primary mover in promoting a career structure for biologists This had not always been apparent. When the President and Chief Executive met with Lord Sainsbury early in the year, one of the problems raised was the increasing use of short-term contracts for postdoctoral scientists. This, sadly, reflects the inherent ageism exercised by bodies like the Wellcome Trust, the MRC and the ICRF among many others, whose grants are simply not available to researchers above a specified age. The year also saw a fundamental change that could well affect biology: the cutback in student grants. If you are reading this as a full Member and Chartered Biologist it is likely that either you had a very wealthy parent, a student grant or a student loan. Without the continuing campaigning of the Institute, the numbers of professional biologists in the UK may well decline as it becomes increasingly difficult to fill undergraduate university places. This is already happening in physics and chemistry. Science is seen as a difficult subject compared with arts and humanities, so if it is also seen as having no career potential as well, many more people will be put off taking up the glorious pursuit of biology.

But this is such an exciting time in biology, who could possibly want to study anything else?

AFTERWORD

Sir Ghillean Prance FRS VMH CBiol FIBiol
Former Director, Royal Botanic Gardens, Kew, and McBride
Professor, National Tropical Botanic Garden, Hawaii

66 This brief history of the Institute of Biology has vividly portrayed a dynamic and growing organisation that is now an important voice of biology in the UK. As the incoming President, I found that the reading of this manuscript could not have been a better preparation for the future. In any institution it is vital to build on past history as new areas develop. This book is rich in fascinating insights into both the recent history of British biology and the politics that have influenced biology. It is an honest appraisal that shows the ups and downs that are to be expected in any growing institution. It is good to have this history written down while many of those who made it are still active and able to tell the story.

I think that many members of the Institute of Biology are unaware of the numerous different aspects with which the Institute is involved on our behalf. It is not just the organ that charters biologists; additionally, it is one of our major voices for addressing issues of current interest to Government. This role of influencing Government policy is one for which all members should be both grateful and supportive. A good example of this is the amount of time that our Chief Executive and other members of the Institute have devoted to the issue of genetically modified foods over the past two years.

These 50 years of the Institute have seen many changes and much progress in the biological sciences. Only three years after the Institute was founded, the structure of DNA was finally elucidated by Watson and Crick. This has led to the molecular work that has revolutionised so many

Professor Sir Ghillean Prance FRS VMH CBiol FIBiol, President 2000–02

aspects of biology, including my own field of systematics. These same 50 years have seen the computer revolution. I now have more memory in my tiny laptop computer than was in the computer on which I did the numerical analysis for my PhD, which filled an entire room. The latest developments that will have a great influence on the next decade are genomics and the understanding of the function of individual genes.

The Institute of Biology has had to adapt to many changes over its first 50 years and there is every indication that this will be a continuing trend. The current research on cloning and genetic engineering, and the development of products from indigenous people's knowledge that raises questions of intellectual property rights, are just some areas that raise profound ethical issues. It is good that there is an Institute to study, debate and influence both scientists and politicians. I foresee a growing rather than a decreasing role for the Institute of Biology and I hope that it will continue to attract new and active members.

I must end by expressing my gratitude to the Editor of this book and the members of the History Networks who have compiled the chapters. Their endeavours have ensured that the details of our history will endure in the future. One of the things that impressed me most as I read this book is the amount of volunteer time that has been given to the Institute of Biology by so many people, especially in the work of our Branches. This volunteer spirit must continue, in support of our most active and efficient staff, if the Institute is to maximise its influence in the future. As the incoming President I very much look forward to working with both the staff and the membership to ensure that the Institute continues to provide for the needs of our members and to present accurate scientific facts to the policymakers of the new millennium. **99**

APPENDICES

Membership totals – the first half-century

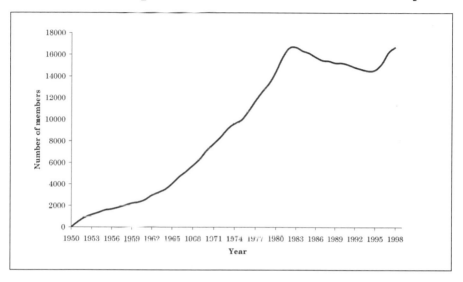

Presidents

Year	President	Year	President
1950–52	E Hindle	1976–77	G E Fogg
1953–54	F E Fritsch	1978–79	R J C Harris
1955–56	Sir James Gray	1980–81	E J W Barrington
1957–58	W H Pearsall	1982–83	J R Postgate
1959–60	A S Parkes	1984–85	J L Harley
1961–62	Sir Gerard Thornton	1986–87	Sir Kenneth Blaxter
1963–64	G E Blackman	1988–89	R W J Keay
1965–66	O E Lowenstein	1990–91	P M Biggs
1967–68	H J Bunker	1992–93	Sir Colin Spedding
1969–71	Sir Frederick Bawden	1994–95	F A Hibbert
1972–73	K Mellanby	1996–97	R B Heap
1974–75	J Heslop-Harrison	1998–99	J R Norris
		2000–	Sir Ghillean Prance

Vice-Presidents

Year	Vice-Presidents			
1953	Sir James Gray	J Hammond	T A Bennet-Clark	H J Bunker
1954	T A Bennet-Clark	H J Bunker	E C Dodds	C F A Pantin
1955	E C Dodds	C F A Pantin	G E Blackman	N W Pirie
1956	G E Blackman	N W Pirie	J B Cragg	M E Varley
1957	J B Cragg	M E Varley	Sir Gerard Thornton	W B Yapp
1958	Sir Gerard Thornton	W B Yapp	E A Parkin	M Robertson
1959	E A Parkin	M Robertson	R J C Harris	P F Wareing
1960	R J C Harris	P F Wareing	A Bishop	N E Hickin
1961	A Bishop	N E Hickin	G E Fogg	J N Davidson
1962	G E Fogg	J N Davidson	H J Bunker	K Mellanby
1963	H J Bunker	K Mellanby	W H Dowdeswell	I A Preece
1964	W H Dowdeswell	I A Preece	M Abercrombie	C G C Chesters
1965	M Abercrombie	C G C Chesters	W V Harris	J C Kendrew
1966	W V Harris	J C Kendrew	P W Brian	C E Ford
1967	P W Brian	C E Ford	L Broadbent	J W G Lund
1968	L Broadbent	J W G Lund	E J W Barrington	P H Gregory
1969	E J W Barrington	P H Gregory	D J Crisp	G Pontecorvo
1970	D J Crisp	G Pontecorvo	J A Freeman	F R Winton
1971	J A Freeman	F R Winton	J H Humphrey	H L Kornberg
1972	J H Humphrey	H L Kornberg	H O J Collier	T G Onions
1973	H O J Collier	T G Onions	Sir Kenneth Blaxter	J Heslop-Harrison
1974	Sir Kenneth Blaxter	D G Davey	R J C Harris	W H Dowdeswell
1975	R J C Harris	W H Dowdeswell	D G Davey	M Brook
1976	R J C Harris	M Brook	J R Norris	C A Wright
1977	J R Norris	C A Wright	D C Breeze	P N Wilson
1978	D C Breeze	P N Wilson	B A Newton	D F Hollingsworth
1979	B A Newton	D F Hollingsworth	A J Abbott	J P Hudson
1980	A J Abbott	J P Hudson	D W Straughan	A MacLeod
1981	A MacLeod	D W Straughan	F J Ebling	G E Russell
1982	F J Ebling	G E Russell	W F J Cuthbertson	P T Haskell
1983	W F J Cuthbertson	P T Haskell	J G Phillips	H W Woolhouse
1984	H W Woolhouse	J Edelman	R M Laws	M Sussman
1985	J Edelman	M Sussman	A J Beardmore	J V Lake
1986	A J Beardmore	J V Lake	D M Conning	H W Grenville
1987	D M Conning	H W Grenville	D Anderson	W W Fletcher
1988	D Anderson	W W Fletcher	F Brown	R J Terry
1989	F Brown	R J Terry	J A McFadzean	C R W Spedding
1990	J A McFadzean	C R W Spedding	J M Dewdney	P B Gahan
1991	J M Dewdney	P B Gahan	T H Maxwell	P N Wilson
1992	T H Maxwell	P N Wilson	M J Llewellyn	R K S Wood

1993	M J Llewellyn	R K S Wood	E S Carter	K R L Mansford
1994	E S Carter	K R L Mansford	B A Callingham	Rev M J Reiss
1995	E S Carter	R L Mansford	B A Callingham	Rev M J Reiss
1996	B A Callingham	Rev M J Reiss	M W Elves	P R Shewry
1997	M W Elves	P R Shewry	S A Turner	Sir Colin Spedding
1998	S A Turner	Sir Colin Spedding	M W Elves	P R Shewry
1999	S A Turner	Sir Colin Spedding	D R Berry	P Caligari
2000	D R Berry	P Caligari	T Tetley	J Lewis

Honorary Secretaries

Year	Honorary Secretary
1950–53	J L Danielli
1954–56	G E Fogg
1957–61	H J Bunker
1962–66	L Broadbent
1967–71	T G Onions
1972–75	P N O'Donoghue
1976	D C Breeze
1977–79	K W Thomas
1980–84	J A Beardmore
1985–89	J C Marsden
1989–92	D J McLaren
1992–95	P N Wilson
1996–	P J Bunyan

Honorary Treasurers

Year	Honorary Treasurer
1950–54	R J C Harris
1955–59	NE Hickin
1960–64	W V Harris
1965–69	J A Freeman
1970–74	M Brook
1975–78	A J Abbott
1979–83	M Sussman
1984–85	B A Newton
1986–92	C Arme
1993–98	A G Cadogan
1999–	M W Elves

General Secretaries / Chief Executives

Year	General Secretaries
1950–51	A Fielding Clarke
1951–82	D J B Copp
1982–88	P N O'Donoghue
1989–97	R Priestley
1997–98	M Fowler (acting)
	Chief Executive
1998–	A D B Malcolm

Charter award

Year	Recipient
1981	K Mellanby
1982	W H Dowdeswell
1984	F J G Ebling
1985	L Broadbent
1986	T G Onions
1989	J C Smyth
1992	R J Terry
1993	M W Holdgate
1995	C Arme
1998	J A Barker
1999	B Dixon
2000	S A Turner

Major Institute Symposia and Conferences

Date	Symposia/Conference	Location	Institute Division
October 1950	Biological hazards of atomic energy (with Association of Atomic Scientists)	London	
April 1952	Biology as a career	Birmingham	
September 1952	Biology and productivity of hot and cold deserts	London	
October 1952	Biology as a career	Edinburgh	
October 1953	Biology and productivity of the sea	London	
April 1954	Training of biologists	London	
September 1954	Factors affecting the numbers of man and animals	London	
September/ October 1955	The biological aspects of the transmission of disease	London	
April 1956	Some problems in host-parasite specificity	London	
September 1956	The biology of ageing	London	
October 1957	The biological productivity of Britain	London	
April 1958	Freezing and drying (with the Wellcome Trust)	London	
September 1958	The effects of pollution on living material	London	
October 1959	Biological hazards of disease control	London	
September 1960	The biology of space travel	London	
October 1961	The better use of the world's fauna for food	London	
April 1962	The training of biologists	London	
September 1962	Colour and life	London	
October 1963	Aggression in animals and man	London	
October 1964	Climate changes in Britain	London	
May 1965	Biological careers	London	
September 1965	The biology of man-made lakes	London	
September 1966	Biology and the manufacturing industries	London	
September 1967	The problems of birds as pests	London	
September 1968	Biology and ethics	London	
September 1969	The optimum population of Britain	London	
September 1970	Future training and employment of biologists	London	
September 1972	Biology of brains	London	
September 1973	The biology of urbanisation	London	
September 1974	Racial variation in man	London	
April 1975	Safety in the biomedical laboratory	London	Biomedical
September 1975	Visual perception	London	
November 1975	Biological resources for food production in Britain	London	Agricultural
September 1976	Effects of pesticides (with the Linnean Society)	London	
November 1976	Biological aspects of farm waste	London	Agricultural
September 1977	Population control by social behaviour	London	

November 1977	Agricultural developments in Australia	London	Agricultural
December 1977	The contribution of scientists to medicine	London	Biomedical
January 1978	Fish farming and wastes (with Institute of Fisheries Management; Society of Chemical Industry)	London	
September 1978	Monitoring the marine environment	London	
September 1979	Vegetables for feeding people and livestock	London	
September 1980	Biology, society and choice	London	
November 1981	Medical Genetics	London	Biomedical
November 1981	Animal Welfare in agriculture	London	Agricultural
March 1982	Conservation of genetic resources	London	Environmental
April 1982	Ecology and evolution	Manchester	Education/ NW Branch
November 1982	Ecology and evolution	Edinburgh	Education/ Scottish Branch
February 1983	Man's parasitic burden	Belfast	
March 1983	Wetlands under threat?	London	Environmental
June 1983	Some current trends in biological education	Newcastle	Education
November 1983	Aspects of cancer biology	Southampton	Biomedical
March 1984	Weather, woodlands and water	Edinburgh	Environmental
September 1984	Conservation with agriculture – a viable partnership	Newton-Abbot	Agricultural/ Environmental
June 1985	Active learning in biology	Cardiff	Education
March 1986	Trees and shrubs in the urban environment	W'hampton	Environmental
September 1986	Agriculture and food research	Rothampstead	Agricultural
November 1986	The caring biologist – biomedicine today	Edinburgh	Biomedical
March 1987	Agriculture surpluses: Environmental implications	London	Environmental
April 1987	Biological consequences of the Chernobyl disaster	London	Biomedical
November 1987	Physiology, medicine and human performance	London	Biomedical
March 1988	Conservation in action	Reading	
March 1988	Since Silent Spring	Cambridge	Agricultural/ Environmental
April 1988	Macro effects from micro quantities (with Royal Society of Chemistry)	Kent	
September 1988	Ecotoxicology (with British Toxicology Society)	Oxford	Biomedical
April 1989	Food and farming: the role of biology	London	
October 1989	Teaching science to children with special needs	Reading	Education
March 1990	The impact of biotechnology in agriculture	Cambridge	
March 1990	Renewable energy and the natural environment	London	Environmental
April 1990	Biology in the National Curriculum	Leeds	Education
November 1990	Food-borne infections. current perspectives	Edinburgh	Biomedical/ Scottish Branch
March 1991	Roads and the environment	Leyland	Environmental

April 1991	Biological consequences of global warming	Plymouth	
April 1991	Britain's contribution to international agriculture	London	Agricultural
April 1991	Links between schools and industry	Loughborough	Education
April 1991	History of BSE	London	History Cttee.
May 1991	Assessment in biological education	Paisley	Educational
September 1991	Evolution of Pure Water	London	History Cttee.
November 1991	Healthcare screening – the future	W'hampton	Biomedical
April 1992	Biology in Europe	Southampton	
October 1992	Ethical issues in biomedical sciences – Animals in research and education	London	Biomedical/ Education
January 1993	Using the school grounds for teaching biology	Loughborough	Education
March 1993	Integrated pollution control : The scientific requirement	London	Environmental
April 1993	Recent advancements in human genetics	Chester	
April 1993	Edward Jenner and Vaccination	Berkeley	History Cttee./ W Branch
June 1993	Gilbert White (with Gilbert White Museum)	Hampshire	History Cttee.
November 1993	Animal farming and minerals	Harpenden	Agricultural
December 1994	Membrane protein trafficking (with BBSRC)	London	
April 1995	A matter of life	Birmingham	History Cttee.
November 1995	Charles Darwin	Down, Kent	History Cttee.
March 1997	Are natural therapies safe and effective? (with Pharmaceutical Sciences Group)	London	
March 1999	John Ray (with John Ray Trust; Society for the History of Natural History)	Braintree	History Cttee.
October 1999	The biology of air pollution (with British Association for Lung Research; British Society for Immunology)	London	
March 2000	Clean technology: industrial: sustainability through biotechnology	London	
May 2000	Century of Genetics (with Royal Horticultural Society)	London	History Cttee.

Institute Branches

Beds, Essex and Herts

Previously part of the London and Home Counties Branch, the Beds, Essex and Herts Branch was formed in 1972 and had around 500 members at the time of formation. Regular events have included Fungal Forays, Symposiums (*Careers in Biology, Ecology of Hertfordshire, Genetic engineering,* … to name but a few), Entomological Field Days, and lectures. The present committee is chaired by Shirley Greatrex, Hugh Loxdale is Branch Secretary, and Kishore Teelanah Treasurer. The Branch had a successful and busy year in 1999. In March, Jim Hope of the Institute of Animal Health, Compton gave a talk on *Mad*

Cows, Mice and Men detailing recent research on BSE. In November, the new Director of IACR Rothamsted, Ian Crute, spoke about *Rothamsted 2000: Science for Sustainable Agriculture*. Membership of the Branch has now reached 935 members.

Devon and Cornwall

The Devon and Cornwall Branch was founded in September 1970 and currently has 293 members. The first meeting took place in December 1970 at the University of Exeter, where it was agreed that the main Branch objectives should be to promote cooperation between biologists in Devon and Cornwall. Over the last 30 years the Branch has held meetings, lectures, symposia, field meetings and student and careers conferences to carry out this aim.

Two field meetings are worthy of mention, one to Powderham Castle on the behaviour of fallow deer and the other to Lundy Island which contains the only Marine Nature Reserve in England. Two founder members of the Branch have been remembered, Norman Holme who was the inspiration behind the development of the Marine Centre near Plymouth and Alison Leadley Brown who was the first secretary and a driving force within the branch for many years.

East Anglia

The East Anglia Branch of the Institute of Biology was inaugurated on 5 November 1965. Magnus Pyke gave an illustrated lecture on *Whisky Research — an exercise in Applied Biochemistry*. Those present then resolved to ask Council to agree to the formation of an East Anglian Branch and elected a provisional committee with K Mellanby as Chairman and P Robson as Secretary. The East Anglia Branch had 148 members at the time of formation, which has risen to 881 in 1999. Sadly, due to lack of support, the Officers of this Branch decided to resign in Autumn 1998 and cease all Branch activities. Although temporarily out of action, the Institute is working towards reforming this Branch.

East Midlands

The East Midlands Branch covers the counties of Derbyshire, Leicester, Lincolnshire, Northamptonshire, and Nottingham and has 800 members. The Branch was formed at a meeting on 22 March 1969, when it was decided to split the Midland Branch in to East and West. The first meeting took place in July 1969.

Everyone on the committee takes a turn in organising meetings, adding variety and interest, which last year included a Castle boat trip, a Great Green Picnic, a talk on the cutting edge of dentistry using light instead of a drill, an excellent fungal foray and a talk on whales and dolphins. The biggest event of the year, involving more than 200 people, was a lecture by Steve Jones on *Is Human Evolution Over?* (The answer is 'yes' he says). In addition we run annual events including the Award for Biological Excellence for practical research, a photographic competition, a Who's Who in the East Midlands, an annual Chairman's Dinner and Careers Fair.

Kent, Surrey and Sussex

The Kent, Surrey and Sussex Branch has 1539 members and was formed in 1972. The inaugural meeting was held on 12 October 1972, where Kenneth Mellanby spoke about the Stockholm Conference. Committee meetings are held at the Marie Curie Foundation which is situated near the borders of the three counties. As well as providing programmes of meetings for its own members, the Branch has been active for many years in planning joint residential meetings with other Branches. The first, an ecological weekend on the Isle of Purbeck, with the Wessex and Thames Valley Branches, and the latest with the Thames Valley Branch in Oxford.

A major activity has been that of giving advice on careers in biology to school pupils and teachers. The Branch has organised its own careers convention with speakers from a wide range of biological professions and the University of Surrey has presented, since 1983, an annual course for teachers and sixth-formers in biological subjects, in cooperation with the Branch.

London

The London Branch covers the Greater London area and has 1134 members. It was founded in 1953 and originally covered London and the Home Counties. It was decided to divide this Branch into four smaller and more practical Branches in 1972 (London and Middlesex; Beds, Essex and Herts; Kent, Surrey and Sussex; and Berks, Bucks and Oxon). The Branch was temporarily closed down in the mid 1970s due to lack of support, but was revived in 1979. The first meeting of the newly revived Branch was on 30 May 1979, where Sir Hans Kornberg spoke on *Agriculture and Pollution*. A notable event was a trip to Rheims in 1980 hosted by the Rheims Biological Society which included several champagne tastings! A meeting held in 1984 on Information Retrieval of Environmental Chemicals, held jointly with the Royal Society of Chemistry, was so heavily subscribed that it had to be moved twice in order to find a venue large enough to accommodate everyone. The Branch has continued to thrive with carefully focused programmes in collaboration with other societies.

London Teachers' Group

The London Branch is unique in having a London Teachers' Group which organises conferences, training, and competitions for teachers and schools. The annual essay competition for schoolchildren attracts many high quality entries.

Mid-Wales

The Mid-Wales Branch was inaugurated on 6 November 1965. The meeting held in the University College of Wales, Aberystwyth was chaired by P F Wareing. A H Bunting gave a lecture entitled *Gentlemen and Players in Biology*. Following a talk on the work and publications of the Institute by the General Secretary D J B Copp it was decided to form a Mid-Wales Branch. P F Wareing was elected Chairman with D R Humphreys-Jones as Honorary Secretary. The first meeting was a symposium entitled *The Biological Efficiency of Crops and Farm Animals* where J P Cooper and W Charles Evans spoke on Crops and Farm Animals respectively.

Covering the counties of Dyfed and Powys, this Branch has a membership of 126 (the branch had only 24 members in the year it was formed). The Branch runs an annual competition for the best and most original Honours Biology Student Project for which all students opting for a research-based project are automatically eligible. The winners receive an award of £100 and a framed certificate. Many successful activities have involved collaboration with either the Biological or Agricultural Societies of the University or the West-Wales Wildlife Trust. Summer visits have proved successful and included Middleton Hall National Botanic Garden of Wales and the Bronydd Mawr Research Centre.

North Wales

On 23 May 1964 a meeting was held at the University College of North Wales, Bangor to inaugurate a North Wales Branch of the Institute. The meeting, chaired by P W Richards, was addressed by J Heslop-Harrison who gave a paper on *The Changing Pattern of Biological Teaching*. D J B Copp gave a brief talk describing the work of the Institute and, at the General Meeting which followed, it was decided to go ahead with the formation of a North Wales Branch and a constitution for the Branch was approved. D J Crisp was elected Chairman and D J Griffiths Honorary Secretary/Treasurer. The Branch had only 32 members in its first year, whereas it now has 161. The Branch covers the counties of Gwynedd and Clwyd. One notable event was the Christmas lecture and buffet held in December 1998. Bruce Ing gave an excellent talk on the *Natural history of Christmas*.

North Western

In 1954 Council approved the formation of the North Western Branch which was to cover the north west of England from the English/Welsh Border at Chester in the south to Cumbria in the north. One of the first meetings was a symposium on Fresh Water Biology held on 16 October 1954 in Liverpool, where the speakers included T T Macan, J W G Lund, H B N Hynes, and J W

Jones. Another early meeting, held on 6 November 1954 in Manchester, was Hormones in Plants and Animals, with Chester Jones, E J W Barrington, J Bentley, and P F Wareing speaking. On 16 October 1975 the Branch held its 21st Birthday celebration meeting in Liverpool. J Heslop-Harrison spoke on *The Pollen-Stigma Interaction: A plant recognition system in action.*

Now with 1138 members the yearly programme of events includes a schools quiz and Christmas lecture, and a family day to Blackpool Zoo. Visits to the Patterson Cancer Research Centre at Christies Hospital and a Fungal Foray have also been part of our calendar.

Northern

The Northern Branch covers from the Tees to the Scottish Border and from the North Sea to the Pennines. It was founded on 11 January 1964 and J B Cragg was elected Chairman. The first meeting dealt with *The Biological Aspects of Water Pollution* and was attended by 60 people. The Charter Lecture for 1993 was given by Rev Audrey Elkington on *The Double Helix and the Trinity* which explored ethics and the current state of play in biology. The 1999 Charter Lecture, given by Roy Anderson, dealt with *The BSE Epidemic, Science, Politics and Policy* to an audience of 300. The present Chairman is Donald Lee and the Branch has 333 members.

Northern Ireland

The Northern Ireland Branch covers the whole Province, was founded in 1958 and currently has 300 members. In Belfast on 13 February 1958, members and prospective members gathered to hear the General Secretary, D J B Copp talk on the work of the Institute. After which the Northern Ireland Branch was formed and G M McCourt was elected Honorary Secretary.

Staff at the Queens University, University of Ulster, and the Department of Agriculture have been very active in developing a full, interesting and informative programme of events. This usually takes the form of one or two symposia, conferences, several lectures, and prize award ceremonies. There are sound links with other organisations such as the Institute of Food Science and Technology and the Royal Society for the Protection of Birds.

Annually the Branch awards individual prizes to the top three students in the CCEA, GCE A-level Examinations (cheque and an Institute scroll); the Maxwell Memorial Prize is awarded to the top student in the HND Applied Biology, each year.

Scotland

The Institute of Biology's second major conference on *Careers in Biology* was held in Edinburgh in 1952. The organisation of the event brought together biologists in Scotland, and led to the formation of the first of the Institute's Branches: the Scotland Branch. Definitely one of the larger Branches, in February 1978 the Branch celebrated its 1000th member, W Jones of the Forensic Science Unit of Strathclyde University. An official presentation was made by Curtis Gemmell at a meeting in Glasgow. The Branch currently has almost 1500 members.

The Scottish Branch is heavily involved with all aspects of Biology in Scotland, but, especially, and traditionally, with education. In 1999, the new Scottish Parliament has meant additional responsibilities for the branch. For the last four years the branch has held Stirling Meetings for teachers throughout Scotland. Highly successful, with over 200 people attending in 1999, this event is going to continue annually.

South Wales

Some 70 members of the Institute and their guests attended a meeting in University College, Cardiff on the 17 December 1965, at which the decision to inaugurate a South Wales Branch was taken. Considering the Branch had only 79 members at the time this was a remarkable turn out. The meeting was opened with an address by C E Ford FRS on *The Ubiquitous Biologist* in which Ford discussed a variety of research problems illustrated by his own experiences. A provisional committee was elected with G F Asprey as Chairman and J Greig as Secretary.

One of the first meetings held by this Branch was on the 17 September 1966 and was attended by over 40 members and their guests. Peter Kelly, organiser of the A-level Biology Section, Nuffield Science Teaching Project gave an excellent lecture outlining the aims of the A-level biology project and giving details of the scheme now in use. This was followed by a lecture by D E Hughes on *Biological Engineering*. Hughes showed how the use of microorganisms enabled man to maintain and control his position in nature. Some intriguing examples were given both of techniques now being developed and possible future solutions to such problems as world food shortage and space exploration.

More recently the Branch hosted a talk at the University of Cardiff on *Biodiversity and Conservation in the Tienshan Mountains* by Vladimir Kolbintsev, Chief Scientific Officer for the Absu-Dzabaghly National Nature Reserve. The Branch covers the counties of Gwent, Mid Glamorgan, South Glamorgan and West Glamorgan and currently has 331 members.

Thames Valley

The Thames Valley Branch covers Berkshire, Buckinghamshire and Oxfordshire and was formed on 1 November 1972. This Branch was one of the four formed when the London and Home Counties Branch divided. Previously called the Berks, Bucks and Oxon Branch, this Branch did not get its present name until December 1987 when Council decided to get rid of the rather unwieldy title. There are 860 members in the Branch and meetings are usually held at the University of Reading. The first Branch lecture was given by George Cansdale and the best attended lecture in the history of the Branch was given by Professor David Bellamy in 1974. The most recent lecture, on dormice, was given by Dr Pat Morris of Royal Holloway College in January 2000.

Wessex

The Wessex Branch got off to a lively start with an Inaugural Meeting on the 25 November 1966. It was held in Southampton University — geographically the centre of this Branch which covers the counties of Dorset, Hampshire and the Isle of Wight. Professor Michael Swann addressed this meeting (at which about 100 members and interested biologists were present) and stimulated considerable discussion on the subject *Biology and Government Support of Science.*

The Branch now has 811 members. In the past three years the Branch has held workshops on A-level biology topics run by local teachers and researchers. Guided tours have been arranged which visited a number of outdoor locations scattered across the region so that they are easily accessible to all members. Some joint meetings have been held with the Devon and Cornwall Branch which have been useful and enjoyable. The Branch Committee remains strong with members across a range of ages and from different biological backgrounds.

West Midlands

On 4 October 1952 at a meeting in the University of Birmingham it was unanimously agreed 'that a Midland Branch of the Institute of Biology should be formed.' A provisional committee, chaired by E J W Barrington, organised the first meeting on 9 May 1953. The Branch held numerous symposia and meetings over the years which were occasionally low in attendance. This was put down to the large area covered by the branch and, over the next 17 years, there were calls for this large Branch to be split. Finally in March 1969 a General Meeting gathered to make a decision. This resulted in the formation of East and West Midlands Branches.

The West Midlands Branch covers Herefordshire, Shropshire, Staffordshire, Warwickshire, and Worcestershire and currently has almost 1000 members. Annual Charter Lectures have been held every November since 1980 and have attracted some excellent speakers. Sir Alec Jeffreys explained his work on genetic fingerprinting; G F A Harding demonstrated his work on Magnetoencephalography; and John Durrant reviewed the development of biology in the Twentieth Century.

Western

The Western Branch covers the counties of Somerset, Gloucestershire and Wiltshire and was founded on 14 November 1964. Two meetings were held in 1964, the first with a Film Show attended by 140 people and followed with a lecture by Magnus Pyke on *Food for the Future*, which attracted an audience of 70. The first Chairman was G C Ware of the University of Bristol and the Chairman for 2000 is Chris Hunter of the University of the West of England. Some events in recent years have included: Farm visits to look at the practicalities of biomass energy production; a visit to Smiles Brewery to investigate brewing to traditional methods; and a talk on *Cloning and Biodiversity* by John Woolliams of the Roslin Institute.

Yorkshire

Although perhaps not the most dispersed of the regions, the Yorkshire Branch nevertheless covers a wide geographic area. The county of Yorkshire contains key cities such as Hull, Leeds and Sheffield as well as having large areas of virtually uninhabited moors. Inevitably therefore, many of those attending events organised by the Yorkshire Branch will have travelled some distance. Nevertheless, attendance of 100 or more is not unusual. The Branch currently has 774 members.

The request for a Yorkshire Branch came from members present at a meeting in Sheffield on 13 November 1954 on marine mammals. The speakers at this meeting were Robert Clarke and R J Harrison. On 20 January 1955 Council agreed to the formation of this Branch.

Yorkshire has always been an active branch and over the years the number of events has grown considerably. An annual symposium and a summer visit are traditional events and more recently a series of talks were organised for Science Week which was attended by about 650 children. To lead us into the 21st century, the Yorkshire Branch has set up its own website (which can be accessed via the Institute webpages) where details of forthcoming and past events can be found.

International Biology Olympiad Teams

Yr	Team			
1998	James Donnely (Gold), Oakham School Rutland	Emily McGee (Silver), Cheltenham Ladies College	Ethan Sen (Silver), King Edwards's School Edgbaston	Daniel Wise (Bronze), Portsmouth Grammar School
1999	Claire Bulmer (Silver), Cheltenham College	Natalie Coltman (Silver), The Perse School for Girls in Cambridge	Henry Evans (Bronze), King Edward's School in Birmingham	Tristan Martin (Bronze), Gravesend School in Kent
2000	Zillah Boraston (Bronze), Kendrick School Reading	Rupert Griffiths (Silver), Winchester College	Tomas Welsh (Bronze), Royal Grammar School, Guildford	Christopher Wilson (Bronze), Dane Court Grammar School

Medals awarded at the International Competition are given in brackets.

Studies in Biology

No	Title	No	Title
001	Ecological Energetics (Phillipson)	035	Temperature and animal life (Hardy)
002	Life in the Soil (Jackson and Raw)	036	Nervous systems (Usherwood)
003	The Study of Behaviour (Carthy and Howse)	037	Photosynthesis (Hall and Rao)
004	An introduction to parasitology (Wilson)	038	The biology of pollution (Mellanby)
005	Plant Taxonomy (Heywood)	039	How trees grow (Morey)
006	Microecology (Cloudsley-Thompson)	040	Endogenous plant growth substances (Hill)
007	Guts (Morton)	041	Hair (Ryder)
008	The body fluids and their functions (Chapman)	042	The structure and function of enzymes (Wynn)
009	The electron microscope in biology (Gristone)	043	Introductory statistics for biology (Parker)
010	Translocation in plants (Richardson)	044	Biology of aphids (Dixon)
011	Muscle (Wilkie)	045	Biology of the food industry (Barnell)
012	Plant breeding (Lawrence)	046	An introduction to animal breeding (Bowman)
013	Chemistry of the cell (Barker)	047	Experimental psychology: an introduction for biologists (Jeeves)
014	Plants and water (Sutcliffe)		
015	Develolpmental plant anatomy (Gemmell)	048	Plants and mineral salts (Sutcliffe and Barker)
016	Plant symbiosis (Scott)		
017	Fungal parasitism (Deverall)	049	Estuarine biology (Barnes)
018	Population dynamics (Solomon)	050	Pest control and its ecology (van Emden)
019	Chemical communication (Ebling and Highnam)	051	The ecology of small mammals (Delany)
020	Human genetics and medicine (Clarke)	052	Phytoplankton (Boney)
021	Cell division and heredity (Kemp)	053	Bone and biomineralisation (Simkiss)
022	Animal Skeletons (Currey)	054	The biology of plant phenolics (Walker)
023	Investigation by experiment (Heath)	055	Anthropod vectors of disease (Busvine)
024	Animal growth and development (Newth)	056	The biology of slime moulds (Ashworth and Dee)
025	Animal photoperiodism (Lofts)		
026	Natural history of infectious disease (Boycott)	057	Dormancy and the survival of plants (Villiers)
027	The membranes of animal cells (Lockwood and Lee)	058	Ecology of plants in the tropics (Janzen)
		059	The optical microscope in biology (Bradbury)
028	The biology of respiration (Bryant)	060	The secretion of milk (Mepham)
029	Size and shape (McNeil Alexander)	061	The biology of eucalypts (Pryor)
030	Cellular radiobiology (Lawrence)	062	Marine zooplankton (Wickstead)
031	Chloroplasts and mitochondria (Tribe and Whittaker)	063	Homeostasis (Hardy)
		064	Diseases in crops (Wheeler)
032	Fungal saprophytism (Hudson)	065	Plant tissue culture (Butcher and Ingram)
033	Animal flight (Pennycuick)	066	Lichens as pollution monitors (Hawksworth and Rose)
034	How grasses grow (Langer)		

No	Title	No	Title
067	Animal asymmetry (Neville)	100	Cellular recognition systems in plants (Heslop-Harrington)
068	Phytochrome and plant growth (Kendrick and Franklands)	101	Sulphur in biology (Anderson)
069	Genetics and adaptations (Ford)	102	The biology of helminth parasites (Lyons)
070	Popular cytogenetics (John)	103	Sex hormones and behaviour (Slater)
071	A biology of locusts (Chapman)	104	Biological clocks (Brady)
072	The dynamics of competition and predation (Hassell)	105	Liver (Horner Andrews)
073	Mammalian odours and pheromones (Stoddart)	106	Aquaculture (Reay)
		107	Pollen and allergy (Knox)
074	Decomposition (Mason)	108	Animals and stress (Archer)
075	Viviparity (Hogarth)	109	Lizards - a study in thermoregulation (Avery)
076	Ecology of fishes in tropical waters (Lowe-McConnel)	110	Sexual incompatibility in plants (Lewis)
077	Ecology and archeology (Dimbleby)	111	Microorganisms and man (Noble and Naidoo)
078	Animals for man (Bowman)	112	Life at high altitude (Heath and Williams)
079	The biology of weeds (Hill)	113	The nature of toadstools (Ingold)
080	Colonisation of industrial wasteland (Gemmell)	114	Nerves, brains and behaviour (Messenger)
081	The social organisation of honeybees (Free)	115	Vocal communication in birds (Catchpole)
082	An introduction to animal tissue culture (Sharp)	116	Influences on animal growth and development (Batt)
083	The genetic code (Clark)	117	Collagen: the anatomy of a protein (Woodhead-Galloway)
084	Lysosomes (Dean)	118	Social behaviour of animals (Deag)
085	Science and fisheries (Cushing)	119	Medical mycology (English)
086	Plants and temperature (Sutcliffe)	120	The respiration of higher plants (Opik)
087	Evolution in modern biology (Edwards)	121	Ecology of insect-plant interactions (Edwards and Wratten)
088	The biology of mucor and its allies (Ingold)	122	The ecology of streams and rivers (Townsend)
089	Life in sandy shores (Brafield)	123	The biochemistry of pollution (Ottaway)
090	Antibiotics and antimicrobial action (Hammond and Lambert)	124	Light and plant life (Whatley and Whatley)
091	Boreal Ecology (Pruitt)	125	Lipids and polysaccharides in biology (Furth)
092	Nitrogen fixation (Postgate)	126	Bioenergetics of autotrophs and heterotrophs (Anderson)
093	Haemoglobin (Maclean)	127	Invertebrate respiration (Wells)
094	Principles of human nutrition (Taylor)	128	Immunobiology (Inchley)
095	Structure and function of viruses (Horne)	129	Growth regulators in crop production (Luckwill)
096	Plant growth analysis (Hunt)	130	Evolution and pollution (Bradshaw and McNeilly)
097	Man - hot and cold (Edholm)		
098	Plant physiological ecology (Etherington)		
099	The physiology of diving in man and other animals (Hempleman and Lockwood)		

No	Title	No	Title
131	The evolution of eukaryotic cells (Tribe, Whittaker andMorgan)	150	Monotremes and marsupials (Dawson)
132	Biological control of pests and weeds (Samways)	151	Ageing (Davies)
133	Ecological evaluation for conservation (Spellerberg)	152	Malaria (Phillips)
134	Molluscs and man (Boyle)	153	Biological fuels (Lewis)
135	Neurons and synapses (Jones)	154	Wetland ecology (Etherington)
136	Biotechnology (Smith)	155	Stomata (Martin, Donkin and Stevens)
137	The growth of leaves (Dale)	156	Carrion and dung (Putman)
138	The biology of parasitic protoza (Baker)	157	Fertilization in animals (Dale)
139	Ecology of rocky shores (Brehaut)	158	Animal hormones (Buckle)
140	Biology of yeast (Berry)	159	Mycorrhiza (Jackson and Mason)
141	Nutrition and health (Taylor)	160	The blue-greens (Fay)
142	Plasmids (Day)	161	The biology of earthworms (Wallwork)
143	Animal taxonomy (Goto)	162	Genetic engineering in higher organisms (Warr)
144	Neo-Darwinism (Berry)	163	Animal reproduction (Cohen and Massey)
145	Sound and hearing (Rosenberg)	164	Human Skin (Wood and Bladon)
146	The colour of animals (Vevers)	165	Seed physiology (Bryant)
147	Insect pheramones (Birch and Haynes)	166	Plants and nitrogen (Lewis)
148	Cell growth and division (Wheatley)	167	Blood sucking insects (Service)
149	Toxicology (Pascoe)		

New Studies in Biology

Year	Title	Year	Title
1991	Introductory statistics for biology (Parker)	1999	Essentials of animal behaviour (Slater)
1991	Pest Control (van Emden)	1999	Microbiology in action (Heritage, Evans and Killington)
1994	An introduction to genetic engineering (Nicholl)	1999	Photosynthesis (Hall and Rao)
1996	An introduction to the visual system (Tovée)		
1996	Biotechnology (Smith)		
1996	Introductory microbiology (Heritage, Evans and Killington)		
1998	An introduction to parasitology (Matthews)		
1999	An introduction to applied biogeography (Spellerberg and Sawyer)		

Modern views in biology

Year	Title
1986	Cell biology (King)
1993	Controlling reproduction (Hutchinson)
1997	The economic importance of insects (Hill)

Open University Series

Year	Title
1987	Animal cell technology: principles and products (Butler)
1987	Biotechnology: the biological principles (Trevan)
1987	Enzyme technology (Gacesa)
1987	Fermentation, kinetics and modelling (Sinclair)
1988	Genetic transformation in plants (Walden)
1989	Fermentation biotechnology: principles, processes, products (Ward)
1989	Plant biotechnology in agriculture (Lindsey)
1990	Biosensors (Hall)
1990	Biotechnology in the food industry (Tombs)
1990	Biotechnology of biomass conversion (Wayman)
1990	Principles of biotechnological engineering (Jackson)

A selection of other Institute publications

Year	Title
1987	Enzymes in industry and medicine (Bickerstaff)
1987	Human genetics and medicine (Clark)
1987	Nitrogen fixation (Postgate)
1988	Biotechnology (Smith)
1988	Control of crop diseases (Carlile)
1989	Genes and gene regulation (Maclean)
1989	Phytoplankton (Boney)
1996	Biosciences graduate handbook (Westlake)
1997	Biosciences graduate handbook (Westlake)

The Institute also produces Careers and Degree guides and other occasional publications.